To Tawaa

This is a true story.
I hope you and your
son enjoy it.

Graham Fields
1st Edition

STANISLAW

STANISLAW

The Butcher's Secret

Graham Fitch

Inkwell Productions

ISBN#: 0-9728118-2-6

Library of Congress Control Number: 2003104823

Published by
Inkwell Productions
3370 N. Hayden Rd., #123-276
Scottsdale, AZ 85251
Phone (480) 315-9636
Fax (480) 315-9641
Toll Free 888-324-2665
Emailo: info@inkwellproductions.com
Website: www.inkwellproductions.com

*To my wife and daughter
who encouraged me to
write this book.*

Table of Contents

Prologue

Stanislaw died in Seattle, Washington, on December 6, 1966. He spent most of his life working as a butcher at the Seattle Public Market. For those who have not visited Seattle, our public market is world famous and one of the last in the United States. It is located at the end of Pike Street in the heart of downtown Seattle, and is often referred to as the Pike Place Market. For over 100 years, farmers, fishmongers, butchers, florists and artists have sold their wares in open stalls that are rented from the city by the day, week or year. Stanislaw occupied a small butcher shop towards the back of the market for nearly 50 years until his death in 1966.

Stanislaw was a lonely bachelor who lived by himself in an old hotel a few blocks from the market. At the time of his death, I was his attorney and when summoned to his deathbed by his landlady, I discovered an army footlocker under the bed of my deceased friend that contained more than $450,000 in U.S. currency. He had no known heirs.

This is the remarkable story of what happened to Stanislaw's life savings.

I was born and raised in Seattle. My father was a Seattle lawyer who represented Stanislaw for nearly 30 years before I became a lawyer and joined my father's firm.

My grandfather was a Washington lawyer who became a United States District Court Commissioner for the Western District of Washington. When I was admitted to the Washington Bar Association in 1962, I was one of the first third-generation Washington lawyers to practice in our state.

I have told Stanislaw's story at numerous family gatherings and I have shared it with countless lawyers and judges who have inquired about the unusual and fascinating Stanislaw saga. My wife and daughter were my inspiration to write this novel and share this story with you. I represent this story as fiction as I have embellished the story with different names, monetary amounts and locations to protect the privacy of the individuals involved. I changed the main character's last name to Taylor, a traditional name from my father's family. The underlying story is based on a true account of my probate of Stanislaw's estate.

– *Graham Fitch*

CHAPTER ONE

MY EARLY YEARS WITH STANISLAW

I first met Stanislaw Stocowski when I was about 9 years old. It was the day before Thanksgiving in 1946. My dad took me with him to visit Stanislaw's butcher shop at the Seattle Public Market. My dad was a lawyer who helped Stanislaw out of legal problems from time to time.

The purpose of our trip was to collect a legal fee from the Polish butcher for getting him out of jail. Stanislaw had recently been arrested for beating up a pickpocket who tried to steal his wallet. It happened on a Saturday night in October 1946. Stanislaw had been drinking, and when he left the bar, he must have looked drunk. The pickpocket thought he had found an easy mark until one of Stanislaw's huge hands crashed into the side of his head and put him in a coma for two weeks. When the unidentified pickpocket came to, he left his hospital room in the middle of the night. Since there was no complaining witness at Stanislaw's arraignment, Dad had the charge of disorderly conduct dismissed.

It was just before lunch when we traveled into downtown Seattle in my dad's 1941 Buick. We parked on First Avenue and Pike Street near the entrance to the 20-

acre public market. We walked past row after row of brightly colored vegetables and fruit all polished and shiny in their meticulously maintained stalls. Toward the back of the market was a small butcher shop that belonged to Stanislaw.

There were several people in front of Stanislaw's shop. We were standing in the rain just outside the green awning that hung over the meat counters. Dad found a spot under the awning to squeeze into. Stanislaw was a huge man. He was well over 6 feet tall with a barrel chest and gigantic arms. When I first saw him, he was behind the glass display counter with a meat cleaver in his hand and bits of dried blood all over his white apron. I began trembling and slid a little closer to my dad. I was trying not to look at the rows of dead ducks, chickens and turkeys hanging over the counter. They had a blood-fresh smell to them and I began to suffer a queasy, seasick feeling. I desperately did not want to embarrass my dad in front of his client by throwing up.

Stanislaw was having an argument with an elderly oriental lady. He was speaking in a calm voice to this angry woman and she was shouting at him in a language I could not understand. The argument was about a duck she had purchased. Stanislaw saw Dad first and winked at him. He then greeted me with one of the biggest smiles I had ever seen. He strolled out from behind the counter and with a sweep of his giants arms placed me right on top of his meat case. He said in a booming voice to his customer, "My

lawyer and his son have come to negotiate your problem."
With a big laugh, he said, "You handle it, Graham, while I
talk with your dad."

I forgot my queasiness as I tried to understand the
lady's problem. I thought she wanted a bigger duck. As
they were all the same price, I took one off the overhead
rack and traded it for the one in her sack. She gave me a
smile, bowed slightly and quickly disappeared. When Dad
and Stanislaw finished their conversation they came over to
see what I had done to make the irate customer go away. I
proudly told them my solution, hoping for heaps of praise.
What I got instead was a belly laugh from Stanislaw that
could be heard throughout the market and a cocked eye
and smirk from my father. I had just given the old woman
a fresh duck for one that was a week old. Stanislaw slapped
me on the back with a laugh and said, "Graham has fixed
the problem by giving away a perfectly good duck for one
that was worthless."

As soon as he stopped laughing, Stanislaw went into
his meat locker and brought out the biggest turkey I had
ever seen. He gave it to my dad and said, "I hope your family enjoys this special turkey that I have saved for you." He
thanked me for getting rid of the annoying customer, and
as he turned away he doubled over in laughter once more.

The "duck exchange story" was one that Stanislaw
never let me forget. He reminded me of it every time I saw
him and always told it with a lot of laughter. I always knew
I would do something nice for Stanislaw to repay him for

my inexperience in duck salesmanship.

On the way home we wondered whether the turkey would fit in our oven; it did with one-half an inch to spare. It weighed 32 pounds. It is the best Thanksgiving dinner I can remember.

Through the years, Dad performed various legal tasks for Stanislaw. When he came to our office, our butcher always brought in a roast, a large turkey or a plump duck. I always knew when our Polish butcher had been in to see Dad, as the same evening we would have a special meal that ended with a toast to our compadre. I became friends with Stanislaw through numerous trips to the public market with my parents. My friendship with him continued through high school when I would visit him after class or on weekends. He had a special knack for sensing when something was troubling me and often had very sage old-world advice to help me solve whatever problem I was having. He helped me several times in situations that I didn't feel comfortable sharing with my parents. I considered him my godfather; he was always glad to see me and he always had time to talk.

Stanislaw lived by himself. We invited him over for dinner on several occasions, but he never came. I graduated from Garfield High School in 1954 and that fall became a freshman at the University of Washington. By taking extra classes and attending summer sessions, I was able to get sufficient credits to be admitted to the University of Washington law school in September of 1957. I turned out for

ROTC, and when I graduated from law school in 1960, I was commissioned as a second lieutenant in the United States Army and went back to the East Coast for training. I was so busy with college in the years from the fall of 1954 to the spring of 1960 that I rarely saw Stanislaw. I stopped by the market every couple of months to say hello and share an occasional lunch with him

He attended my graduation from law school. After the ceremony as we were mingling with our families, he surprised me with a present. It was wrapped in white butcher paper and tied with white butcher twine. I didn't open it until later but when I did, I realized how much I meant to him. He gave me his gold pocket watch with a cover that popped open to display a picture of Stanislaw in his World War I uniform. The package also contained a Bible covered in old well-worn black leather. There was a short note on the inside cover from Stanislaw. He told me that this was the Bible he carried in France in 1916. To this day, I guard these treasures and pull them out for special occasions to reminisce about Stanislaw.

In December 1960 I was on Christmas leave from the army and I came back to spend the holidays with my parents. Dad and I went down to the butcher shop to see Stanislaw and get a standing rib roast for our Christmas dinner. I hadn't taken the bar exam yet but Stanislaw called me Lawyer Graham anyway.

He grabbed me like he did the first time we met and raised me off my feet in a big bear hug. He told me over and over how proud he was that I had graduated from law school and was a real lawyer who could continue protecting him like Dad had all these years. Stanislaw was also happy to hear that I was in the U. S. Army. He closed his market and announced that he was going to take his lawyers to his favorite bar to celebrate. We went to a small pub in the market and for several hours listened to Stanislaw talk about his Army experiences. He enlisted in 1916 and was immediately sent to the Western Front in France. Within days of his arrival, he was poisoned by mustard gas and left for dead on the battlefield. Sometime later he was found in a trench by friendly troops and sent to a U.S. Army field hospital in England.

He learned English at the hospital and became a helper in the hospital kitchen. After a few months, an opening occurred in the hospital butcher shop and he took the job. For the rest of the war he stayed in England and became an accomplished butcher. After the war he came to the United States and finally ended up in Seattle. When he saw the Seattle Public Market, he knew he had found the place to open his shop.

It was near dusk when I paid the bar bill over Stanislaw's objections. We headed home with a magnificent roast and some new stories about our family butcher.

After Christmas I returned to my army duty station, which was the counter intelligence corps school at Fort Hollibird, Maryland. The base was a top secret U.S. Army intelligence school located in a suburb of Baltimore. I was a second lieutenant and was being trained by the army to be a prisoner interrogator. The whole country in the early 60s was sure that a communist was hiding in every closet and it was our job to find them. The most important lesson I learned in two years with the army was that a successful interrogator starts sentences with one of the basic inter-rogatories: **WHO, WHAT, WHEN, WHERE, WHY** or **HOW**. If you start a question with one of these words, the person being questioned will give a narrative answer rather than just a yes or no response.

I eventually transferred to Ft. Lewis, Washington, and joined the ultra elite 4th Military Intelligence Detach-ment of the 4th Infantry Division. I became the Security Control Officer of the 4th Infantry Division and was in charge of all Division security clearances. My duty at Ft. Lewis could be best described as long periods of extreme boredom broken up by frequent drunken bashes staged at our secret, fenced intelligence headquarters. Eventually I was assigned to Camp Mercury, Nevada, for security work at the army atomic tests detonated in the spring of 1962. As soon as the tests were over, I requested 60 days' leave and returned to Seattle. During that time, I passed the Wash-ington State Bar Exam and became the 3rd lawyer in our family. When my leave was over I returned to my unit and received a commendation for my work in Nevada with a promotion to first lieutenant. My commanding officer begged me to remain in the service as he enjoyed having his own lawyer. I took the promotion and applied for discharge as my two-year duty tour was up. The day I got out of the Army had to be one of the happiest days of my life. When I returned to Seattle, I worked for two years as an Assistant Attorney General for the State of Washington. I learned more in two years about practicing law than most lawyers do in a lifetime. When I entered full-time private practice in 1964 I was a seasoned trial attorney.

I joined my father's firm and was immediately put in charge of litigation. Although our firm still technically represented Stanislaw, the old butcher stayed out of trouble and only came into the office for occassional social visits. I always went by his shop when I was in the market, but by now he was working part time and usually wasn't there. Stanislaw hired a young man to run the butcher shop and cut his own time at the shop to a day or two a week. Just before Thanksgiving in 1966, Stanislaw dropped off two large turkeys at our office. He enclosed a note indicating that he was going to retire and take life a little easier. When Dad saw the turkeys and the note, he mentioned that Stanislaw was having some health problems and that he had helped the old butcher sell his business to his helper. The next time we heard anything about Stanislaw was on December 6, 1966.

CHAPTER TWO

STANISLAW'S DEATH

On December 6, 1966, I learned that Stanislaw had passed away. I was at home listening to the evening news when my answering service called with what they perceived was an emergency. The landlady at the small hotel where Stanislaw had lived for over 35 years called me and said she had not seen him for several days, and when she used her pass key to get into his room, she found him dead in his bed. She knew he had recently sold his shop to his helper and retired. She said Stanislaw had been going downhill immediately after the sale of his shop. He was drinking heavily and then disappeared for several days. After not seeing or hearing from him for three days, she entered his room and discovered his body.

The landlady was a loving, caring Japanese woman who had been taking care of Stanislaw for the 35 years that he had been staying in her hotel. Her name was Keiko Natsumuara and she was one of the first persons Stanislaw had met when he arrived in Seattle. There was never a romantic relationship between the two as she had a husband and a fine family. Keiko and Stanislaw were good friends and they genuinely cared for each other's well-being. The hotel was small: 20 rooms on the second floor of a retail store. It was about three blocks west of the public market and within easy walking distance to Stanislaw's butcher shop. Keiko regularly made breakfast for Stanislaw and it was very natural for her to be concerned when she hadn't seen him for several days. She sounded terribly frightened when she called my office and wanted me to come over immediately, before the police arrived. I left my apartment and got to the hotel just as the police arrived. Keiko led us to Stanislaw's room and I entered with the police.

Stanislaw had passed away in his sleep. The old butcher was lying on his bed and looked like he was taking a nap. He was over 80 years old, but no one knew for sure because he never talked about his family, his age or what he had done before coming to Seattle. The few times he mentioned his family to Keiko, it was only to say that he had had no contact with them since the First World War and that he didn't trust them. His belongings consisted of a dresser full of work clothes and a few suit jackets in the closet. Under his bed was a footlocker with a padlock on it. It was an old Army footlocker about 4 feet long, 2 feet wide and 2 feet high. We found a set of keys on the dresser and there was a key that fit the padlock. With the police watching, Keiko and I opened the footlocker. It contained an upper box or tray-like shelf that was divided into two parts. On the left-hand side there were several packets of old letters and postcards that were tied with a ribbon. The right-hand side held an old Bible similar to the one he had given to me on my graduation. There was also a beautiful set of mother-of-pearl rosary beads lying next to the Bible and a small silver crucifix.

We lifted the tray from the foot locker and were astonished to find dozens of stacks of U.S. currency neatly arranged in bundles of 20 dollar bills. We counted more than four hundred and fifty thousand dollars of U.S. currency with some of the bills being at least 50 years old. Keiko quickly explained that Stanislaw had told her that he had lost several thousand dollars in a bank failure in 1929 and had never trusted banks since.

The police called the King County Coroner and in about 20 minutes the coroner and his deputy arrived. The body was quickly removed. Keiko signed documents agreeing to Stanislaw's transfer from the County Morgue as soon as a funeral home could be found to arrange for his burial. Being a Roman Catholic, cremation was out of the question. Keiko indicated that she would arrange for a suitable funeral service at St. James Cathedral in Seattle.

The police offered to take custody of the money. I quickly objected, declaring that my client, Keiko, was the personal representative of the estate and that she would file for probate in King County Superior Court. I explained that the money would be protected for the creditors of the deceased and would pay Stanislaw's burial expenses, with any remainder distributed to his heirs or the State of Washington if he had no heirs. This seemed to satisfy the police and they left.

Keiko had not been paid rent for six weeks and, as such, she was the major creditor of the probate and had the legal right to apply for appointment as the personal representative of Stanislaw's estate.

In less than three days I had all the legal work done and Keiko was appointed as the personal representative of the estate. She arranged for an appropriate memorial service at the cathedral. It was attended by her family, our family and a few merchants from the Seattle Public Market where Stanislaw had his shop. Stanislaw was laid to rest in Northwest Cemetery in a special section reserved for veterans of World War I. The area was beautifully landscaped, and we all mentioned that Stanislaw's final place on this planet was very special. The U. S. Army, through the Veteran's Administration, made all the arrangements.

Stanislaw had a full military funeral complete with an Army Honor Guard that fired a gun salute for him. On the way home from the burial service, Keiko and I promised each other that we would find the family that Stanislaw left behind when he left Poland 50 years ago.

CHAPTER THREE

DUTCH WILLIAMS

Our only source of information about Stanislaw's past was the packet of letters that we found in his footlocker. They were all a half century old and in Polish. We also knew that he was Roman Catholic and had served in the U.S. Army in World War I. We had an inventory of $457,325 in cash which we put in an interest-bearing savings account at a local bank. In 1966, that amount of money in cash and in small bills, found in a footlocker was newsworthy. It resulted in a front-page newspaper article on December 20th saying that we were looking for the heirs of our "wealthy deceased butcher" who apparently distrusted everyone and banks in particular. It also brought out the attorneys from the escheat division of the State of Washington. Escheat is a fancy word for giving to the state tax coffers any money left behind by someone who died with no heirs and no will.

Rick Riplinger, an Assistant Attorney General for the State of Washington, called me and indicated that he was going to file a petition for removal of the funds to state custody until we had produced a bona fide ascending or descending ancestral heir. He demanded to have notice of any probate petitions.

Washington law provides for the distribution of property, with judicial approval, if the decedent dies without a will. First the surviving spouse is considered, and if none, children of the deceased come next. If there are none, the decedent's parents inherit if they are alive. If the parents pre-deceased the person dying, the next line of kin by Washington inheritance law is brothers and sisters of the decedent with the children of any deceased brothers or sisters taking the place of the parent and sharing equally the parent's share. The statute goes further and spells out cousins, second cousins and even allows going back up the family tree to provide for the descendants of brothers and sisters of the parents and grandparents of the decedent. Often there are no records and heirs cannot be verified to the satisfaction of the Washington Probate Court. When this occurs, and when the search for all heirs is exhausted, the state takes the decedent's property under the State of Washington escheat laws. There is no limit on the length of time a personal representative can look for heirs as each estate is different and the timing on approval of inheritance or delivery of the funds to the State under the escheat law is solely within the discretion of the probate judge assigned to the case.

It was imperative that the estate was assigned to a friendly probate judge or we risked having the State of Washington impound Stanislaw's money. If that were to occur, it would not be released until a bona fide heir came to Washington and proved his or her right to inherit Stanislaw's estate. As long as we still had control of the money, we could petition the court for distribution to heirs in Poland if we found some to exist. If the court agreed with our investigation, it had the power to order the funds released to the heirs without requiring them to travel to Washington.

In 1966, King County Superior Court had 22 separate judicial departments, one of which was the probate calendar. Each Superior Court judge is assigned to sit on the relatively boring Probate Bench for a 30-day stint. This meant that of the 22 or so King County Superior Court judges, each judge draws a month of "probate duty" about once every two years. Although the assigned probate judge gets off the probate bench at the end of his or her assigned month, any cases of special interest could be followed by the same judge for months or years even though the judge had returned to civil or criminal case assignment in his or her regular courtroom. These conscientious judges would continue to preside over the cases that originated during their assignment to the probate calendar. This applied only to cases that needed their special attention because of their knowledge of complicated facts surrounding the particular case.

My first thoughts were to try to get the estate assigned to a judge that wouldn't bend to pressure from the State of Washington Escheat Office. An older judge that wasn't looking for any favors from the governor would be ideal. I knew that the escheat department of the State of Washington had already laid plans to sieze Stanislaw's life savings.

We were in luck. It just so happened that in December of 1966 Judge Sigfried "Dutch" Williams was on the probate bench. My dad and Judge Williams were classmates in law school at the University of Washington and after graduation and a few years in private practice they spent four years in the Army Judge Advocate Corps together. They both were full "bird" colonels when they left the Army and they both spent the rest of their lives ordering people around as Army Field Grade Officers tend to do. Judge Williams was one of the most feared judges on the bench to every young lawyer, except me. My dad and Dutch Williams were fraternity brothers and lifelong friends. He treated me like his favorite nephew and I was always glad to be in his courtroom.

I knew that I needed to file my Petition for Probate of Stanislaw's estate before Judge Williams before he left the probate bench in January. I knew he would do whatever I wanted as long is it was authorized by statute and within his discretion to do so. He was scrupulously honest and would not break the law. He was nearing retirement age and was the spitting image of the classic description of a judge that was described to us in law school:

Every new judge when elected decides his or her cases during the first 10 years on the bench with a fear that they are making a wrong decision. For the next 10 years they decide each case with the conviction that they are absolutely correct. After they have spent 20 years on the bench they decide each case with a growing indifference as to whether they are right or wrong and when it becomes habitual, they retire.

In the week after Christmas, 1966, Keiko and I made our first court appearance. Rick Riplinger, had petitioned the court for an order impounding all the estate funds. I counter-petitioned for payment of expenses and release of some estate funds to start an heir search. Dutch Williams stormed in from his chambers and in a booming voice demanded to know what was so damned important that it wouldn't keep until after the holidays. Rick made the mistake of trying to confuse the court by presenting his petition as if it was an emergency. Judge Williams told him to take his petition and "stuff it where the sun don't shine."

He then turned to me and asked how my family spent Christmas. He chatted for about five minutes about his memories of a Christmas long ago with my dad on Guam in 1943. He leaned back in his chair and rambled on about how they had Spam and cranberry sauce at the officer's mess. He said one of his favorite World War II pranks was when he snuck up and snapped a picture of my dad sitting on the officer's three-hole outhouse. It was a big pipe with butt-size holes drilled in it and no roof. It was outside behind the officer's mess hall. Dad was trying to void himself of the terrible holiday Spam feast. Dutch laughed and said Dad offered a 10 dollar bill for the roll of film. Dutch refused and said that he was going to post the photos in the Army courtroom for all the prisoners to see. He never mentioned that he didn't have any film in the camera. For the rest of the war, Dad thought Dutch had the pictures and was always worried about when they might show up. Even after the war he would tease Dad about how he was going to use the photos. I listened patiently to the story that had been told at every Christmas party I had attended with my dad and Dutch Williams since they returned from their military duty.

He looked down at me from his bench and like a kindly department store Santa Claus said "What can I do for you, Graham?" I explained the circumstances and advised that I wanted court approval for paying Keiko's creditor's claim and the funeral expenses and asked that he release $1,000 of the estate money for legal expenses to conduct a mail and telephone search for heirs. I told him that we would keep the rest of the money in an interest-bearing savings account that would be released only by further court order. He approved our plan and signed the order I presented. As we were leaving his courtroom, he told me to come back if I needed any more money. Then he stood up and as he left the bench he pointed a finger at Rick Riplinger and said in a loud voice, "Buster, don't you ever bring a petition like that into this courtroom again or you will be on my permanent KP list." Rick sneered at the judge and luckily for him, Dutch didn't see the gesture of disrespect.

I relaxed, and as I looked at Keiko's grateful smile, we both knew that we were in good hands in Dutch Williams' court. We then put our heads together and decided how to best solve the dilemma of the missing family of our deceased client.

Pike Place Market

CHAPTER FOUR

THE SEARCH FOR INFORMATION

Our first attempt to locate Stanislaw's family was to try and interpret the packet of letters found in the foot-locker. They were all in Polish and very faded. Many had water spots and a few had entire pages obliterated by water damage. I went to the University of Washington and met with Professor Dupont who was in charge of the foreign language school of the university. It was winter break at the university, but he promised to question the returning professors in late January to see if any of them could translate the Polish letters. I was satisfied that this was probably the cheapest and quickest way to get the letters translated. I left copies of the letters with Professor Dupont.

Our next efforts involved an inquiry to the Department of the Army in Washington D.C. We also sent a request to the Veteran's Administration asking for any records either facility could provide on a U.S. Army soldier named Stanislaw Stocowski who enlisted in the U.S. Army in 1916. I received a reply from each agency within a week. Each reply envelope contained sets of forms for release of information. The forms required the signature of Stanislaw Stocowski, our deceased client. I sent back copies of the court order appointing Keiko as Personal Representative. About 20 days later I got a letter from the Department of the Army saying that only the next of kin could request this information and since Keiko was not related, they could not release any of Stanislaw's army file.

The Veteran's Administration reported that they had no file on Stanislaw. Apparently he had never applied for any Veteran's benefits. I went back to Judge Williams' courtroom and waited until there was a recess in the case he was hearing. We went to his chambers during his mid-morning break and I explained that the Department of the Army refused to provide any information unless it was requested by the next of kin and we still had been unable to locate any "next of kin." He agreed that the Army records were important and picked up his phone and instantly cut through the miles of red tape separating me from the information I needed. He called the general in charge of the Department of the Army Records Section at the Pentagon. Dutch knew him by his first name. They had served together in Washington, D.C. after the war. He could not have been more helpful after Dutch told him why we wanted the information.

Within 10 minutes I got all the information the Army had, including some notes in the Stanislaw Stocowski file that we never would have seen in a normal records search. Once again I was reminded that it's not what you know, but who you know that makes otherwise impossible tasks easy.

The records that were released showed that Stanislaw Stocowski enlisted at the age of 18 in February 1916 at an army recruitment tent in Copenhagen, Denmark. The recruitment "notes" added that he was responding to a poster he had seen in Warsaw, Poland, offering U.S. citizenship to any Polish citizens who would enlist in the U.S. Army and serve for the duration of the war. His original enlistment forms were in Polish but they did list his next of kin as his mother and father, several brothers and a sister. The forms stated that all of his immediate family reside in Lanski, Poland.

He was sent to France where he was trained to fire a Springfield rifle. Two weeks later he was sent to the Western Front to serve on the infamous Maginot Line, the dreaded death trenches of World War I. The records confirmed what Stanislaw told me about being poisoned by mustard gas in the trenches in the fall of 1916. When he was found alive on the deserted battlefield he was revived and was evacuated to a field hospital in England.

After his release from the hospital, the following spring, he was assigned to a hospital kitchen that prepared meals for the patients at the hospital. He was promoted to private first class and assigned to the hospital butcher shop as an apprentice butcher. He was a fast learner and became a journeyman butcher. After the war, he was honorably discharged and given passage on a returning troop ship that arrived in New York in the spring of 1919. When he left the ship with his citizenship papers, he left no forwarding address. This was the last information the Army had concerning Stanislaw.

I thanked Judge Williams for his help and decided that the translation of the letters found in the footlocker was our best hope for finding Stanislaw's family. About two weeks later I got a call from Amy Sorenski, a Polish student attending the University of Washington. Professor Dupont had given her the letters as she was the only Polish student who recognized their contents. The letters were written in a Polish dialect that stumped the faculty, but she recognized it as a version of the Polish language she saw as a student in Warsaw. She said it came from an area about 160 miles southwest of Warsaw, close to the Russian border. The Polish words were mixed with Russian, which made it hard to translate. She spoke both languages and agreed to spend the weekend translating the letters in exchange for a fee of $50. She said that she would have all the letters translated for me by the following Monday.

I called Keiko and she agreed to meet me at my office the next week to review the translations. On the following Monday, Amy came into my office with a complete translation of the seven letters. She went over them in detail with us and helped us form functional translations in English that conveyed the basic content of the letters. After finishing the translation explanation, she thanked us for the opportunity to help. She collected her $50 and left.

Keiko and I went to lunch at Ivar's "Acres of Clams," a Seattle landmark. Over lunch we read and re-

read all of the letters at least three times. When we had finished, we sat back with a sigh of relief; for the first time we saw a glimmer of a chance of keeping Rick Riplinger and his gang of bureaucratic escheat police from getting Stanislaw Stocowski's life savings. We now had the names of Stanislaw's brothers and sister and a good idea why he hadn't communicated with them for the last 50 years.

Seattle Waterfront
Ivar's Acres Of Clams

CHAPTER FIVE

THE LETTERS

The translations were lengthy and hard to translate into English. Some pages were water stained but they could still be read. With Amy's translations, Keiko and I were able to assemble a fairly reasonable summary of each letter. We reviewed all of the letters, pulling together the thought pattern of the writer, and we agreed that the following transcript was a fair description of the content of the letters Stanislaw kept for so long.

The transcript of the letters follows in the dated order of their postmarks.

Letter No. 1:
> Dated Feb. 10, 1916. No Return Address.
> Addressed to Private Stanislaw Stocowski,
> U.S. ARMY, Brussels, Belgium

Dear Stanislaw,

You broke your parents' hearts when you left Lanski and went to Copenhagen to enlist in the United States Army. You know that you are the only strong one left to help the family. Your brother

Marion is not well and after you left he became very lonely and withdrawn. You don't have any idea how cruel we think you are. How could you leave us? Mother and Father are both sick. They have no money to help them get through this terrible winter. Now that you are a rich Yankee, the least you can do is send us some of your money.

Your sister, Aneskia

Letter No. 2

Dated April 5, 1916. No Return Address.
Addressed to Private S. Stocowski
APO 689, Paris, France

Dear Stanislaw,

I had just about given up hope of ever hearing from you again. Your letter arrived today with the money you sent. Is this all they pay you? This is barely enough to get your parents some fuel so that they can keep warm. They are both very sick and need medicine.

I beg you to send more money now. It isn't fair for you to run away and leave us here to care for your poor parents. The least you can do is send us money.

Your sister, Aneskia

Letter No. 3

Dated June 3, 1916. No Return Address.
Addressed to Pvt. S. Stocowski
APO 689, Paris, France

Dear Stanislaw,

I haven't heard from you since April. The parents of Jorgan just got a notice from the U.S. Army that he was killed in France. Since you and Jorgan joined the Army together we are fearful that you are in France and may be dead or dying from battle wounds. Please write if you are alive.

Your sister, Aneskia

Letter No. 4

Dated: July 31, 1916. No Return Address.
Addressed to Pvt. S. Stocowski
APO 32, Le Havue, France

Dear Stanislaw,

When your letter arrived, Aneskia and I rejoiced as we have heard of how many soldiers are being killed every day in France. We were sure you had perished in the terrible war you are fighting for America. You are Polish and so is your family. Why are you fighting for the Americans?

You have still sent no money. Everyone in Lanski talks about how rich you are now and what a shame it is that you are so selfish with your money. Our parents are dying because you are too cheap to send any more money. If you don't trust us or care for me or Aneskia any more let me know and we will quit wasting the few zlotys we have on postage for the letters we write you. Regardless of how you feel about your brothers and sister, please don't forget about your parents. They are very sick and need your money. Don't abandon Mama and Papa.

You loving brother, Paul Stocowski

Letter No. 5

Dated August 25, 1916. No Return Address .
Addressed to Pvt. S. Stocowski
APO 32, Le Havue, France

Dear Stanislaw,

Mama died in July and Papa was so upset at not hearing from you that he suffered a stroke at Mama's funeral. We had no money to get him to Warsaw for medical care and because of this he died last week. If only you had helped they would both still be alive. The least you can do is send us your share of their burial costs and their grave marker. Aneskia and I have agreed to pay 50 zloty for the funeral expenses and the grave marker and you should pay at least half of it as you know how much money you have and how little we have.

Your loving brother, Marion

Letter No. 6
Dated September 22, 1916. No return Address.
Addressed to Pvt. S. Stocowski
APO 32, Le Havue, France

Dear Stanislaw,

Thank you so much for the Money Order for 150 zoloty. Mama and I went into Pionki and cashed it at the Post Office. We stopped by the church and lit a candle for you. Father Roland asked about you and said he would send a prayer for your safe return. Marion is trying to take credit for getting you to send the money. He claims he tricked you into getting some of your cash. What did he say to you in his letter? The money really helps and Mama and Papa send their thanks as well but you should be ashamed of waiting so long to help your family. Send more every month or you won't have a family to come home to.

You are foolish to risk your life in this ruthless war just so you can be another Polish, unemployed immigrant in America. You have seen how many of our neighbors went to America only to return home because they could not earn a living.
Come to your senses Stanislaw, and help support your family before it's too late.

Love, Aneskia

Letter No. 7

> Dated January 17, 1917. No return Address.
> Addressed to Pvt. S. Stocowski,
> APO 155, Dover, England

Dear Stanislaw,

When we got your letter we were all shocked to learn that you thought our parents had passed away. It must have been dreadful to learn that Marion tricked you into sending money by claiming Mama and Papa were dead. I don't blame you for never wanting to hear from any of us again. Remember we love you and hope you have a good recovery from the mustard gas attack your unit went through. I know you are soon leaving the Field Hospital. I hope you don't really mean what you said in your letter, but if I don't hear from you again, I will understand why.

Love, Aneskia

This was apparently the last communication Stanislaw had with the family he left behind in Poland in 1916. The letters explained why Stanislaw was estranged from his family and provided an important clue in our quest to find his heirs. Prior to reading the letters, we had been unable to locate Lanski on any map of Poland. The sixth letter from

Aneskia told us that the closest town with enough business structure to cash a check was Pionki. The Catholic church they attended was also there. We even had a new name, "Father Rowland" that we might be able to locate through the Catholic Church.

We went to the Seattle Public Library after lunch and with persistence we were able to find Pionki on a well-detailed map of Poland. We did not see Lanski anywhere in the vicinity. Pionki was a tiny town or village with it's name printed in the smallest print imaginable on the map we were examining. It was about 100 miles southeast of Warsaw. We now knew that Lanski was close to Pionki but we didn't know in what direction. In the spring of 1917, Stanislaw had at least two brothers, a sister and both parents still living. We felt that we were finally on the right track.

Next, I contacted the Polish government to ask for their help locating our missing heirs. I thought that nearly a half a million dollars would get the attention of prominent authorities of one of the poorest countries in the world. After weeks of fruitless letter writing and literally dozens of phone calls to the Polish Embassy in Washington D.C., I got the message. Welcome to the Twentieth Century Mr. Taylor. The Polish government could have cared less about my search for the Stocowski heirs. If my interest in Poland did not involve espionage, security, or a breach of their protocol, they didn't have the desire or time to help me. I met with Keiko and we agreed that we would not allow the attitude of the Polish government to weaken our resolve to locate the Stocowski heirs.

Graham Taylor in 1967

CHAPTER SIX

THE LAST ALTERNATIVE

My first round of letters was directed to the Polish Embassy in Washington, D.C., the U.S. State Department and the Polish Government Foreign Inheritance Office in Warsaw. The Polish Embassy sent back the letter saying that they were too busy to look for Polish citizens with U.S. relatives. Their letter stated that if I sent them the estate assets they would get it to the Polish heirs. If this was not acceptable, I was advised to travel to Poland and find the missing heirs myself. They enclosed a visa application and a warning that once I was in Poland I would be subject to Polish security laws. The letter also said that visa approval could take as long as three months.

Since I thought I might eventually have to go to Poland, I filled out the forms, one to the Polish Embassy in Washington, D.C., and one for the U.S. State Department. I feared the Polish government would manufacture heirs to claim the money so I didn't tell them the names of Stanislaw's family. I stated on the Visa application that I wanted to travel to Poland for "business and pleasure." A few weeks later I got a reply asking me to be more specific. I responded that I was a lawyer looking for relatives of my client that lived in Seattle. They seemed satisfied and sent me a two-week tourist Visa.

Our State Department responded to my letter by sending the address of the U.S. Embassy in Warsaw and recommended that U.S. citizens avoid travel to Poland. I was advised that Poland had some of the strictest tourist travel restrictions of any of the Iron Curtain countries. If I insisted on traveling to Poland, they strongly recommended that I check in with the U.S. Embassy in Warsaw as soon as I arrived.

My letter to the Polish Foreign Inheritance Office came back stamped:
"NOT DELIVERABLE AS ADDRESSED"

It wasn't until several weeks later that I learned that the Polish Postal Service routinely returns letters and packages unless the sender uses the Polish spelling of Warsaw: "Warszawa." This was long before postal ZIP codes which now ease this bureaucratic stupidity for today's postage patrons of Poland.

I was frustrated at my lack of progress in locating heirs through the normal information channels. I began to doubt that we would ever transfer Stanislaw's estate to his surviving family.

I mentioned the problems I was having to some friends during a cocktail party in Seattle. The party was at Walter Klinger's beautiful home on the shore of Lake Washington. Walter and I were fraternity brothers and had been friends for years. He was one of the most prominent orthopedic surgeons in Seattle. At about this time, the orthopedic community was having a medical breakthrough with the development of stainless steel implants and hardware for orthopedic patients with severed limbs. The world standard for these prostheses was a company from Warsaw. Walter dragged me across the lawn to a conversation group of doctors who were listening patiently to a tall, handsome, gray-haired, extremely well- dressed man speaking to them in medical terms that only the orthopedists understood. This man owned the Warsaw prosthesis company that made the new implants.

This was my first meeting with the world-famous Dr. Marion Zeiss. We were introduced and I told him that I was looking for heirs in Poland and hoped to find them as I was probating their deceased relative's estate. I said that we had been unable to locate any of our deceased client's family and that we had received little help from the Polish government. I told him about the returned letter that was marked "not deliverable as addressed" and he laughed at my spelling of Warsaw. He said Polish postal clerks love to send back letters for spelling Warszawa without the extra Z in the middle and the A at the end. He went on to suggest that if I paid him expenses for an interpreter in U.S. currency, preferably small bills, he could get his brother to help me find the missing heirs. He said, "My brother works for the Polish government in their missing persons department and has connections that would be very useful to me in my heir search."

His suggestion was impractical and would never get court approval. He scribbled a phone number on his business card and told me to call him when I was in Warsaw. He moved off and was besieged by several doctors trying to learn how they could participate in the stainless steel implant madness.

By now it was late April and almost four months had gone by. Rick Riplinger filed a motion to renew his request to have the money turned over to the State of Washington escheat division.

Keiko and I decided that one of us had to go to Poland, find Lanski and talk with the residents to see if they knew where to find any of the survivors of Stanislaw's family. Keiko felt that an Oriental woman would be at a disadvantage in an Iron Curtain country. It was decided that even though it would be more expensive to send a lawyer, it was the most practical solution to our dilemma. We reasoned that there was sufficient money in the estate and a lawyer would get appropriate legal answers to advise the court whether there were any Stocowskis left that could share the inheritance.

I filed a petition to the court asking for an allowance of up to 5% of the estate to make an heir search. This was about $20,000. This sum would include all expenses and legal fees. The hearing was set for the last Friday in April, before the Honorable Dutch Williams. Rick made such a fool of himself arguing against the petition that Dutch almost placed him in contempt. I got my petition granted and Judge Williams told me that if I was making progress, I could take up to 10% of the estate, but if I did, I better come back with some heirs.

Rick gave oral notice of appeal, but it was 4:40 p.m. by the time the hearing was over and the clerk's office closed promptly at 4:30 p.m. It would be Monday morning before Rick's appeal could be filed. Rick neglected to request a stay of proceedings freezing the status quo while he prepared his appeal.

As we left the courtroom, Dutch invited me to join him that afternoon at the Rainier Club and suggested that I bring my dad with me. The Rainier Club is located in the old financial district of Seattle and is one of the city's oldest businessman's clubs. Nestled in a Victorian brick building, it serves some of the best food and spirits in the State of Washington. It was said that a deal was never made in Seattle that involved more than $50,000. without at least one meeting at the Rainier Club. I went back to the office and told Dad about the court's decision and the invitation to meet Dutch at the club. Dad said he was busy and added, "My old Army buddy just wants me to buy him a few drinks and you can do that." My father did not drink very much and rarely attended after-hours functions where the boys had a couple of shots before going home to their wives. Dad reminded me that Dutch routinely looked for any excuse for free cocktails at the Rainier Club that was conveniently located one block from the court house.

I met Dutch in the men's bar at precisely 5:30. He was halfway through a double Beefeaters on the rocks. He waved a hand in recognition as I walked in the door. I told him Dad had an unavoidable conflict. Dutch nodded his head as if he half expected that his old war buddy would be a no-show. We talked about the weather and politics for a few minutes and then Dutch told me he was going to set a $20,000 appeal bond. He said that until an appeal bond was posted by Rick, I was free to go to Poland on my heir search mission. I told him my bags were packed and I would leave as soon as possible. He grabbed a phone from a nearby table and called information for the SAS airline reservation phone number. After a minute or two he hung up and announced that I should try to catch the overnight SAS plane to Copenhagen, which was scheduled to leave that night at 9.

He patted my hand and with a tear in his eye said, "Have fun and do your job well. I wish I was going with you." He told me to hurry and said our cocktail hour could be postponed. With that, I left and raced to the bank, arriving just before the extended closing hours for Friday expired.

I took $6,000 out of the estate account: $200 in shiny new Kennedy half-dollar coins, $800 in crisp new one dollar bills and the rest in fives, tens, twentys, fiftys, and a few hundred dollar bills. I took $500 out of my personal account and stopped by the office to pick up the firm's American Express card.

I stopped at the candy counter in our building and

bought two boxes of Baby Ruth candy bars for any kids that I might run into on the trip. I took our firm's biggest briefcase and, fortunately, everything fit securely inside. When I got home and grabbed the bag I had packed, my pet cocker spaniel, Maggie, sat at the door, begging to go with me. The best I could do for her was drop her off at my parents' home. They loved her and I knew she would be spoiled rotten by the time I got back. Mom and Dad were worried about my going behind the Iron Curtain alone, but when we talked about the alternatives and the probability that heirs would never be found if I didn't go, they accepted that I had to go. Dad backed out his car and said, "Get in, I'll take you to the airport." We rode in silence for the 20-minute drive. As we arrived at the SAS departure doorway, Dad shook my hand and said, "Stay out of trouble. I don't want to have to travel to Poland to find you." I couldn't tell if he was jealous of my international adventure or sensed danger ahead.

I left Dad's car and ran for the SAS counter without a minute to spare. My tickets were purchased and the ticket counter agent told me to carry my own bags to concourse A, ramp 10. The plane was due to leave in 10 minutes and they were already boarding standbys.

I got to the gate just as they were closing it. I showed the ticket agent my boarding pass. He re-opened the cabin door and said under his breath, "You cut this one a little close, Mr. Taylor." I was so late they had already given my seat away to a standby passenger. All of the coach seats were filled. I thought I would be taken off the flight, but a pleasant SAS flight supervisor appeared and, after learning of the problem, my ticket was upgraded to first class at no charge. The front cabin was almost empty and the seats were twice as big as the coach seats. I slid into an oversized leather seat next to the window, just as the plane's engines roared to life. Within minutes the SAS Boeing 707 taxied out on the main runway. While the plane was on the runway, a slender blonde SAS flight attendant slipped a cold glass of champagne into my hand.

It was only then that I relaxed and began to enjoy one of the great adventures of my life.

CHAPTER SEVEN

SAS TO COPENHAGEN

This was my first trip to Europe. I was on a Polar nonstop flight to Copenhagen where I would make arrangements to fly on to Poland on the Polish national airline, LOT. I was excited about seeing Denmark and Poland and whatever other parts of Europe I could squeeze in after I had completed my job.

The stewardess came back as soon as we had leveled off in flight and offered me a menu. She also brought a cocktail and wine selection that was really quite good for airline fare. I ordered vodka on the rocks and she suggested that I try the Stolichnaya Russian Vodka. I had never heard of it, but, after my first sip, any vodka made behind the Iron Curtain became my drink of choice on the trip. When the stewardess returned with my drink order and a small hors d'oeuvres plate I took my first really good look at her.

She had slender legs and hips. As she handed me a drink and the snack tray, her jacket parted to reveal generous curves under a sheer white blouse. She was probably in her early 20s. She looked like a model with her platinum blonde hair and refreshing smile. She began to unbutton her uniform jacket and then struggled to get it off her shoulders. In the process I observed a body that reminded me of Sophia Loren when she climbed out of the water in "Boy on a Dolphin." The stewardess put on a white service apron and soon was bringing the first course of a four-course dinner. It was lox and capers bordered with caviar. Next came a filet mignon carved from a large roast on a rolling cart. The third course was a complicated salad with exotic greens, pickled herring, and a Stilton cheese dressing. This was my first experience of the European custom of serving the salad after the entree. I chose my dessert from a tray that included French pastries, several flavors of ice cream and a variety of miniature after-dinner drinks.

After dinner, she started a movie and darkened the cabin. It was an old movie starring Jack Lemmon and Marilyn Monroe that I had seen several times. I turned on my reading light and began going through some of the documents in my briefcase. After a few minutes the stewardess asked if I minded if she sat down for her break in the empty seat next to me. Of course I obliged and said I was glad for the company. We introduced ourselves and I learned that her name was Ingried Johansen and that she lived in Rungsted, a small village just north of the city limits of Copenhagen. She had finished the European version of college and got a job with SAS to see the world. She had visited the United States several times and loved every minute she spent in America. She had seriously thought about transferring to the SAS Seattle base.

I asked her about her education and she told me that

public school in Scandinavia and the rest of Europe was similar to a U.S. grade school with two years of high school. After that, students went either to a trade school or attended private two-three-or four-year colleges which were probably like community colleges in the United States. They taught basic skills in English, accounting and business without any specific training for a trade. The end product was a student educated to be capable of low-level administrative, secretarial or government employment.

She graduated from such a college in Copenhagen, having attended two years with a major in English. She immediately applied for a job with SAS and had been a stewardess ever since. She said that her grades were good and she could have continued with her education, but she needed a break. After the European version of a secondary school, gifted students who could afford to go on with their education enrolled in the universities of higher learning throughout Europe and became the doctors, lawyers and other professionals of the European intellectual scene. She thought that she would have gone into medicine if the SAS job had not materialized. When she learned that I did legal work for a large hospital in Seattle, she had a hundred questions for me. I answered most of them and in the process developed a growing attraction to this beautiful woman.

Ingried was single, 24 years old and her fondest desire was to live in California. She had used one of her SAS employee passes to visit Los Angeles the previous summer. She spent her whole vacation lying on the beach and surfing. She could hardly wait to get back. She asked if I was married and I told her that I had come close several times but I was still single. I told her that every time I got serious about someone, something like law school or the military service would intervene and by the time I was through, the girl I was dating had found someone else. She laughed and said that European women were used to waiting for their men. She said that two World Wars had taken the lives of 60% of European men and for the last 50 years most European women had no husbands. She went on to say that her father died in 1943 in Belgium and that she never met him. She was born two months after he died.

Our conversation shifted to what there was to do in Denmark and she recommended several good restaurants in Copenhagen. When I mentioned that I was staying at the Hilton, she said that the Rathskeller in the Copenhagen Hilton was her favorite lounge. It was so pleasant talking with her that in what seemed like a few moments, the movie was over. Suddenly the cabin lights came on and she excused herself and went back to work.

At that time in our flight we were over the North Pole and the sun was just beginning to come over the horizon. From my window seat in front of the wing of the 707, it seemed as though I could see for a thousand miles. There was nothing but white snow and ice. I wondered what would happen if our engines failed and we landed in this barren wilderness. I dozed off, and the next thing I remember was Ingried gently nudging my shoulder. She was holding a breakfast tray.

We had gone through so many time zones that it was 8 a.m. in Denmark. We were about an hour from the airport and a light breakfast was served to those who wanted it. Another stewardess came through the cabin with duty-free cigarettes and liquor. Ingried had told me that I should take Marlboro cigarettes and Jim Beam or Crown Royal with me into Poland because they would be exotic gifts that were not available behind the Iron Curtain. I took her advice and loaded up on as much as I was allowed to take into Denmark duty free.

The plane's captain made a pre-arrival announcement and a short time later the plane came in for a smooth landing. After a short taxi, we arrived at the gate. I loaded up my duty-free purchases and exited the plane. I said good-bye to Ingried and wished her luck on getting to California.

My first experience in a European airport was pleasant. The Copenhagen airport was efficient, clean and quite modern. I was surprised to see armed guards with automatic weapons stationed around the terminal. Apparently Europe was concerned enough about terrorists in the 1960s that every airport was guarded. The guards didn't bother anyone, but you could see that they meant business and everyone passed by them very quietly.

In a few moments we were through customs and immigration and collecting our baggage. I went to the street and hailed a cab. I had forgotten to change any money into Danish krone and as I told the driver to take me to the Hilton Hotel, I began to worry about how I was going to pay him. He spoke perfect English and gave me a sightseeing tour at no extra charge on our drive into town. When we arrived at the Hilton, I explained that I had no Danish krone and he informed me that U.S. currency was the universal currency of Europe. He would gladly take U.S. currency for his fare. I threw in a Kennedy half-dollar coin as a tip and you would have thought I had given him a hundred dollar bill. The Kennedy coins were very rare in Europe in 1967 and a new un-circulated one was worth about $10 U.S.

I suspected this when my banker urged me to take 200 half-dollars with me, but I was still amazed to learn that I could provide huge tips at very little cost. JFK was a very special American to everyone I met on the trip.

I carried my own bags which consisted of a duffel bag, my oversize briefcase and my sacks of duty-free purchases. I had reserved a room in advance from the Hilton World Wide Network in Seattle, and my room was ready on my arrival. I was given my key and shown to my room by a courteous bellhop. I tried the Kennedy half-dollar tip again, and it worked like a charm. By this time I had been awake for 23 hours and as soon as I locked my door, I fell on the bed without even taking my shoes off. I slept for ten hours.

I woke at 8 p. m. and was ravenously hungry. I

changed into jeans and headed for the streets of Copenhagen. My hotel was close to the world-famous Tivoli
Gardens, which are best described as an old-fashioned
Danish version of Disneyland. The Hilton faced Tivoli and
the lights and sounds of families enjoying a Saturday night
in early May drew me toward the park like a magnet. It was
a short walk to the main entrance. This happened to be the
opening weekend of Tivoli Gardens for the 1967 summer
season.

The park is open all year but a lot of the concessions
are shut down in the winter. It was a great time for me to
visit Tivoli Gardens as everything was clean, freshly painted
and the crowds made it easy to spot the good rides and
food stalls. The gardens were lit by beautiful Venetian
lanterns that were hung in the trees. They cast a soft white
light that transformed the park into daylight. There must
have been close to a thousand of these Venetian lanterns as
well as hundreds of conventional lights. It was a bright,
cheerful place full of families. The Danish visitors to the
park were very well dressed. The men wore dark suits and
ties and most of the women were wearing dresses, coats
and hats. The kids were all dressed as if they were on their
way to church. It was a big difference from the way people
came to a park in Seattle. There were lovers everywhere
with nearly every park bench occupied by kissing couples.

After an hour or so I was still hungry and started to
inspect the hundreds of different food stalls in the park.
They were run by single proprietors and not necessarily by

the park employees. The food they served was food prepared by the person running the stand and the variety was
never ending. It was easy to spot the good food stands by
the lines. I tried every kind of hot dog made in Denmark.
There were franks, bratwurst and Polish sausage in every
size, shape and flavor. I tried hot ones, apple filled ones, fat
ones and long ones. They were all good, but the best was
the regular long skinny Danish bratwurst that was always
served in a special roll that looked like a miniature loaf of
French bread.

The park was filled with slot machines that looked
like they were made a hundred years ago. Everything was
mechanical. They paid off in game tokens that could be
traded for prizes but not cash. A Boeing engineer would
have thought he had died and gone to heaven just to watch
these Rube Goldberg machines perform.

A Danish krone is about the size of a quarter and in
1967 you got seven to the dollar. Everything in the park
from the hot dogs to the slot machines cost one krone.
After two hours, I was exhausted and stuffed with enough
food to last me a week. I spent $3.50 and wished something
like this were available in Seattle.

Back at the Hilton, I wrote a few letters and dropped
off to sleep with a promise to myself to go to the Polish airline office in the morning and arrange a flight to Warsaw. I
was having too much fun in Copenhagen and had to get
back to business.

CHAPTER EIGHT

COPENHAGEN

Sunday morning came early. I learned later that the jet lag west to east is much harder than the other direction. I was exhausted after visiting Tivoli Gardens and needed to go to bed. As tired as I thought I was, I couldn't sleep past 1 a.m. no matter how hard I tried. I had a novel and read for an hour and tried again. Same result. After staring at the ceiling for half an hour, I tried reading the book again. About 3 a.m. I felt drowsy and finally was able to sleep for a few more hours. At 6 a.m. I had no further use for sleep and got up and showered. This process continued with an hour a day adjustment until finally my system started running on European time.

I dressed casually and headed for the lobby. It was 7 a.m. and the ground floor of the Hilton was deserted except for a lone employee at the front desk. I asked him where the Polish airline office was located and when it opened. I learned that the ticket office was just up the street and it opened at noon. With five hours to kill, I began to look around Copenhagen. I found a small coffee shop next to the hotel that was open and I sat down at a sidewalk table and ordered an expresso. A newsstand was close by and I got a copy of the Herald Tribune. It was the weekend edition and it carried all the stateside political gossip as well as the previous week's business activity.

The Herald Tribune, European Edition, is the most widely read English newspaper in Europe. It lets all Americans and anybody else who reads English know what is going on in Europe and the United States. I was never disappointed with any Herald Tribune that I bought in Europe and often wondered why you couldn't buy a concise clear newspaper like that in the United States. The paper had everything including a small classified section offering European products to English-speaking readers.

After I finished my expresso, I strolled around the shopping mall that was near the hotel. Most of the shops were closed but I could see that Copenhagen was very fashion conscious. The windows were every bit as colorful and stylish as any department store window in New York. There was a heavy emphasis on furs and even the sweaters had ribbons of mink or lynx sewed into them. Most of the stores opened at noon. I wandered back to the hotel to check on getting a rental car as I thought a drive in the countryside would be a pleasant way to spend the rest of the morning.

The concierge recommended that I rent a car and visit the Little Mermaid, a world famous statue, located in Copenhagen harbor, and then continue driving around the harbor to the delightful little town of Rungsted. It was located just north of the city limits. He said there is a

museum there that is one of the most popular tourist des-
tinations in Denmark. I had not been able to get Ingried
out of my mind since the flight and suddenly this hotel
employee was directing me to visit the village she lived in.
Whether it was fate or "the Devil made me do it," I didn't
care. I wanted to see her again.

I got an Avis rental car and drove toward Rungsted.
It was a beautiful drive with the anticipated windmills
appearing every few hundred meters or so. I was not
expecting them to be so big. Many were easily 10 stories
high. They were right out of Alfred Hitchcock's "North by
Northwest" and I imagined Cary Grant and Grace Kelly
dodging bullets as they ran between them. There was hardly
any wind, but these huge windmills were slowly revolving.
There was nobody around them and no particular homes
near them. Their general purpose was not to generate electricity but to pump water over the dikes to keep the fields
dry. A lot of Denmark, like Holland, was reclaimed from
the sea by building dikes out to sea and then pumping the
water out to reclaim fertile soil that was just below sea
level. The windmills had to keep pumping to keep the low
land dry.

The Little Mermaid was a disappointment at first. It
was so "little" I drove right past it. I saw her in my
rearview mirror and said to myself, "Is that all there is?" I
almost kept going, but didn't. I turned around and stopped
at the small parking lot and walked over for a closer look.
It's small but really worth the stop. It's a seaman's memorial

and several cars stopped and people dropped wreaths in the water at the Little Mermaid's base.

She sits on a rock about 10 feet from shore, and on this Sunday there were about a dozen beautifully colored flower wreaths floating in front of the statue. There were several hundred white swans gliding through the water and it almost seemed that this small bronze figure of a young mermaid was feeding them. The whole scene was straight out of a Disney movie like "Cinderella" or "Sleeping Beauty." The weather was clear but in May it was chilly, probably about 35 to 40 degrees Fahrenheit. I continued to be impressed at how well dressed everyone was.

I got back in the rental car and started driving toward Rungsted. I couldn't help wondering what I would do if I saw Ingried again. I soon saw signs that said Rungsted-Blixen Museum. I was surprised to see it in English. When I came to the little village, I understood, as I found that Rungsted was a tourist mecca with tour buses all over several large parking lots. There were numerous guided tours of the Blixen Museum and most were advertised in English.

The museum was obviously the town's main attraction. Rungsted was originally built as a vacation spot for King Karl XII around 1500 B.C. The town looked like it was 1000 years old. Everything was clean and the bricks of the buildings and the cobblestone streets were clean and well scrubbed. The people of the village dressed in historical costumes. I strolled around with the rest of the tourists.

If I heard someone who looked like a resident of the village speaking English, I asked them if they knew Ingried Johansen. They all knew the SAS stewardess who comes back to visit her mother once in a while but no one had seen her for weeks. They all confirmed that Rungsted was so small that they would know if she was in the village. I gave up the quest and resigned myself to the fact that I probably would never see her again. Still her memory haunted me and I thought of her all the way back to Copenhagen.

I turned in the rental car and walked to the LOT office. I showed them my American Express card and asked for a one-way non-stop flight to Warsaw leaving the next afternoon. The LOT employee at the counter said that there was a plane at noon but I would need a round trip ticket because it wasn't legal to sell a one-way ticket if I wasn't a Polish citizen. I told the ticket agent that I wasn't sure when I was going to return. We finally settled the problem by my buying an open return ticket to Berlin. This was the shortest and cheapest ticket back across the Iron Curtain that I could buy.

Next, the agent demanded to know what hotel I was staying in. I asked for help and was advised that the hotel best equipped to handle Western tourists was the Bristol. It was located near the Warsaw Town Square and many of the hotel employees spoke English. The agent could handle the reservation by telex if I so desired. I booked a room for a week at the Bristol and went back to the Hilton. The

Copenhagen LOT employees were obviously working on a commission as they were all very anxious to make sure I paid for everything in advance, with my American Express card, before I left the counter. They claimed that my credit card might not be good in Poland. I found out later that my American Express card was good everywhere in Europe on both sides of the Iron Curtain. I also discovered at the Bristol Hotel that it was 50% cheaper if I had walked in off the street, rather than have LOT book it for me.

I left the LOT office with my reservations and tickets and headed for the Hilton. I went to my room and checked for messages. There were none. I watched the local news on the television set in my room, but with the language barrier, I could only try to interpret what was going on by watching the pictures of the day's activities. I was particularly shocked by the TV films of the day's Autobahn crashes. It must have been the lawyer in me. Everyone in Europe drives their cars as fast as they can and some of the crashes are unbelievable. On a lot of the roads, there are no speed limits and most of the German and Italian cars are capable of speeds exceeding 150 mph. The detailed crash pictures on TV graphically showed the devastating consequences to the vehicle occupants when an accident happens at high speed.

I started reading my book, but must have dozed off. When I opened my eyes it was almost 9 p.m. I was hungry and realized that I hadn't eaten since I had the breakfast roll and cup of expresso that morning. I looked on the hotel directory for directions to the Rathskeller. It was located in the basement with the entrance behind the elevators on the north side of the building. I followed the directions and found a stairway near the elevators with the Rathskeller sign over it. As I started down the steps, music and good smells drifted up the stairwell. There was a lot of tobacco smoke in the restaurant when I walked in the door and it was hard to see. I was shown to a small table in the corner and I waited for a menu.

There were wine bottles hung from the ceiling with garlands of garlic strung between them. It reminded me of a classic New York Italian restaurant except that everyone in the Rathskeller was much better dressed than the Italian patrons in New York.

As I was looking over the menu I glanced around the room and there she was. My heart skipped a beat. Ingried was sitting at a table across the room and was smiling in my direction. She was with two other women who were also looking in my direction. I walked over and asked if I could join them. I was nervous, frightened and infatuated with Ingried. They invited me to sit down.

The food was good, the company was superb and the Rathskeller turned into a disco about 10 p.m. I paid for everything and the girls were all grateful. I love to dance and I danced the legs off all three of them. Finally about 1 a.m. Ingried's two friends said goodnight and again thanked me for dinner and the fun evening. Ingried and I enjoyed a dance or two, finished our bottle of wine and left the Rathskeller. As naturally as if we had been lovers for several years, we both knew without asking that the night was not over. Ingried leaned on my shoulder as we waited for the elevator.

When we arrived on my floor, we walked slowly to my room and entered. Ingried took my keys, turned and locked the night latch above the regular door lock. I had no experience in dating European women and I was both shy and embarrassed that I didn't know what to do next. Ingried on the other hand was Scandinavian and was raised with no sexual inhibitions whatsoever. It was very natural for her to come into my arms, and before I knew what was happening she was removing my shirt. It happened almost in sequence: first my shirt and then hers, my pants and then her skirt. She did all the work and suddenly we were both standing in the moonlight with nothing on except our smiles. We spent the rest of the night talking, laughing and making love to each other. Ingried was the finest woman I had met up to this point in my life. All women after her were measured by her standard. She didn't care that I was from a city 8,000 miles away and didn't care if this was the one and only night we would ever spend together. All she cared about was that we enjoyed being with each other. I often thought of that night and finally rationalized that European women had lost so many generations of their men in the World Wars that they enjoyed love when it came their way and were thankful for the good times they shared with the men they met in their lives.

On Monday morning, Ingried left early; she had to work a flight to New York. I told her my life in Seattle was busy, but I would love to see her again. She promised to call and say hello next time she had a Seattle layover. She said she didn't like Seattle flights because they were too long but now that she had a Seattle boyfriend she would look forward to our next meeting. With that she dressed, blew me a kiss at the door and vanished. I had been away from Seattle for 48 hours and I felt like a teenager after my first date. What an unforgettable night. I hoped she meant what she said and would call me in Seattle. I would arrange for her to meet all my pals and see the parts of Seattle that make all of us lie to the world about how much it rains there. I knew she would love the city and the places I would show her in and around Puget Sound.

In Memory of Ingried

CHAPTER NINE

WARSAW

It was Monday morning and I was headed toward the airport. The fare was 19 krone and when I tried to pay the driver, he said "Could you skip the krone and give me a couple of those Kennedy split dollars?" Good news travels fast. Apparently every cab driver within a mile of the Hilton Hotel knew I was tipping with Kennedy half dollars. I laughed and pulled two Kennedy coins out of my pocket and gave them to my grateful cab driver.

I grabbed my luggage and headed for the LOT check-in counter. All of the female employees wore heavy make-up. They looked like the ladies behind the cosmetic counters in the big department stores in New York. They smelled of way too much cheap perfume. I showed my tickets and my passport and was assigned a number. When my number was called, I went through a checkpoint and was loaded onto a bus with several other travelers. The bus took us to a plane that looked like one of the last Douglas DC-6 propeller aircraft. It was a Russian-made plane, and it was either fly this to Warsaw or walk. I crossed my fingers and got on board.

The plane was built for 80 passengers, but there

were only about 20 people in the passenger cabin. There were three stewardess' to serve us. They all looked like the LOT female employees at the ticket counter. There was no pre-flight drill and they began serving complimentary drinks as soon as we got on board. No one insisted that we put on our seat belts. It was more or less a, "Take care of yourself" attitude. Our choice of drinks was mineral water, Russian vodka or Polish vodka with stale crackers. I decided to try both the Russian and the Polish vodka and, to my surprise, the Polish vodka was better. I didn't drink very much as I was sure I would need all my brain cells functioning flawlessly when I arrived in Warsaw.

I watched as the other passengers gradually drank themselves unconscious on their way back to their Fatherland. Maybe they needed the alcoholic support to face the harsh reality of life in Poland. We landed at 3:30 in the afternoon and taxied to a spot close to the terminal. We got out and were herded into a small building next to the main terminal. Each of us, one at a time, was taken into an enclosure surrounded by 2-inch thick bulletproof glass. When it was my turn, I went into the enclosure and sat down. I was facing a glass wall with a small slit in it, similar to a mail slot. Although the glass was shaded, I could see the outline of a uniformed guard on the other side. A command in Polish was barked at me from behind the glass and I said, "I only speak English." The voice, much softer, said, "Passport please." I placed my passport in the slot in the black glass and it was sucked inward as if a vacuum had been turned on. I waited for what seemed like 10 minutes but in reality it was probably only a minute or two. Two uniformed officers came into the enclosure where I was sitting and indicated that I was to follow them. We went to a small room with no windows and a third uniformed officer came in and in perfect English said, "Good afternoon Lt. Taylor." He said to me, "Our records list you as a CIC agent." I replied, "I have not been in the U.S. Army for five years." They were still concerned that their records listed me as an active U.S. Army counter intelligence corp. officer.

All three started questioning me at once. They seemed hostile and were obviously concerned that I was entering Poland for some subversive activity. It was a very frightening experience. I showed the court order allowing me to conduct an heir search in Poland, my Bar Association card and explained that I had come to Poland to find Polish heirs who would inherit money from my deceased client who was a U.S. citizen. I told them that if they would not let me into the country to look for the missing heirs, my job was finished. I would go back home and tell the state of Washington government that the three of you would not let me search for Polish heirs. The Washington treasurer would get the money for the State of Washington, instead of Polish citizens. I said, "It would be a shame to let the government take hard-earned dollars that rightfully belonged to some of their fellow Polish citizens." They wanted to know how much money was involved and whether I had brought it with me. The door opened and a porter brought in my luggage. They began to open it. I was nervous about the Marlboro cigarettes, as I was sure I was over the import limit and I didn't want to get arrested for some petty customs violation.

They found the Kennedy half-dollars and looked at them but didn't know what they were and went on to the rest of the papers in my briefcase. I was concerned about their taking some of my estate notes but I suddenly realized that they couldn't read them. They could read typewritten English pretty well but not English handwriting in longhand. I purposefully left nearly all the estate documents in Seattle, taking only the court order permitting me to travel to Poland and my lengthy handwritten notes to guide me on the heir search. This proved to be my salvation. The longhand was like a secret code and they were too proud to admit they couldn't read it.

When they got to my duffel bag, they found the cigarettes and their eyes bulged out in great surprise. I ceremoniously gave each of them a carton. Within minutes they had a small conference and the one with the most embroidery on his shoulders smiled and said, "Welcome to Warsaw attorney, Graham Taylor. May you have a successful trip."

People can say whatever they want to about the evils of smoking, but the Marlboro man saved my bacon on that scary morning in Warsaw. The gifts made me fast friends with the goon squad and I was immediately escorted upstairs like a celebrity. They took me straight through customs without a bag being checked. I actually got to the street ahead of most of the passengers I flew with from Copenhagen. To this day I wonder how they got my Army records.

I needed some Polish money and I went to the foreign currency exchange window, just outside the terminal. I wanted to cash $200 in U.S. currency. My first clue that I was doing the wrong thing was that there was no line. The Polish currency was zlotys and the new zlotys exchanged officially at 17 zlotys to the U.S. dollar. The clerk gave me 3400 zlotys and a weak smile, and I headed towards the cabs parked at the curb. I sensed I had been ripped off and decided to check the exchange rate at a Warsaw bank when I had the chance.

The few cabs outside the terminal were old Mercedes 190 diesel four-door sedans. Only tourists were using the cabs. The fares were set if you were going to the main square, but anyplace else needed a special permit and the fare was negotiable. Most of the drivers spoke English and although there was no cab line as such, they had their own system to decide whose cab the next tourist should get in. I was pointed in the direction of a cab about 20 feet away and I walked toward it. The driver did not help with my bags. I threw them in the back seat and climbed into the passenger seat.

I said that I wanted to go to the Bristol Hotel. He asked for 100 zlotys and I gave it to him. After a few minutes I asked him why we hadn't started and he explained that he needed more passengers. Three men with large bags approached and they got in the back of the cab. They left their bags by the curb and got in the back seat. The cab driver took my bags out of the cab and placed them with theirs. He started to pull away leaving my unlocked briefcase on the curb. It contained all my legal papers and some money. I yelled, "Stop!" and he did. I jumped out just as a truck with the words BRISTOL HOTEL on its side pulled up. Two men in civilian clothes got out of the truck and began walking toward our luggage. I grabbed my briefcase and started back towards the cab. An armed soldier who was standing at the loading zone stopped me and gestured with his loaded rifle, for me to leave my briefcase, with the rest of my bags on the curb.

The cab driver got out and I told him in English that I couldn't leave my legal papers to be delivered by truck. He yelled at the soldier, "Diplomatic, Diplomatic." Hearing that, the soldier retreated and waved as if to say "O.K." Two men started putting the other luggage in the truck. I got back in the front passenger seat carrying my briefcase on my lap. I asked the cab driver what was going on, and he said one word, "Routine." The rest of the trip was spent in silence. The three passengers in back didn't say a word. We drove through the back streets of Warsaw until we finally arrived at a huge open square the size of a dozen football fields. We drove around the eastern edge of the square and stopped in front of a seven-story granite building that was straight out of a Frank Lloyd Wright brochure of the 1930s. It looked more like a theater or library than a hotel, but this was it, the Bristol Hotel. We left the cab, and at the top of the steps leading into the hotel, my luggage and the luggage of the three businessmen stood waiting for us. I mentally placed that in the category of "How did they do that?" and decided I would find out later.

Apparently we were expected. A hotel supervisor bowed and ushered us to the reception desk. He was dressed in a formal set of tails and wearing patent leather shoes, but I noticed that his outfit was worn and ragged at the edges. I surrendered my passport at the front desk as requested, and I was shown to my room. My guide was a young porter in a drab uniform. My impression of the hotel was that I had gone back in time 50 years, and I was at a mortician's convention.

The mood of the place was very somber. My room was ready and it faced the large open square. It had dark wooden walls that had been polished thousands of times. They smelled of furniture polish and had an oily residue on them. Most of the wardrobe was built-in and was the same wood as the walls. The door was 3 inches thick and had a compartment that was accessible by opening a panel from the inside of the room or using a key and opening a similar panel on the hallway side of the door. I opened it from the room side of the door and saw a space for shoes and a place to hang clothes. I checked out the rest of the room: There was a small table with a radio, an antique phone and a hotel directory. The bathroom had a huge 7-foot bathtub with claw feet. The sink was ample but old and the hot and cold-water faucets had been polished so many times that the brass underneath the chrome plate was coming through. I lay down on the bed and to my surprise it was a soft feather bed and quite comfortable.

I had no plan of action and only a vague idea where my deceased client's relatives lived, 50 years and two wars ago. I felt very uncomfortable as a visitor to Poland. I decided to go to the U.S. Embassy in the morning and see if they could help me. I saw in the hotel directory that meals were included in my reservation and dinner was served from 8 to 10 p.m. I soon learned that everyone eats late in Europe.

I was tired and decided to take a short nap. I wanted to take a stroll around the town square before dinner, but to my surprise I slept soundly until almost 9 p.m.

I wasn't hungry as this was a new time zone for me and I was still adjusting. I took a quick bath in the huge tub and threw on some comfortable clothes. In Warsaw, it was still chilly in May, and I threw a sweater over my shoulders to keep warm. I was late and I knew I had to hurry if I wanted to see what a first-class hotel in Warsaw served to its guests for dinner.

CHAPTER TEN

THE BRISTOL HOTEL

I came down to the lobby about 9 p.m. in casual attire and was surprised to find everyone in formal dress. At first I thought there was a wedding or reception of some kind. I spotted the three men who were in the cab from the airport and chanced a conversation with them. They had changed into dark suits and matched the dress of the rest of the crowd. They were Germans from Frankfurt.

They were frequent visitors to Warsaw, selling steel automotive frames to the Polish automobile industry. They were very friendly. When they learned I was an American, they each had questions they wanted answered about the United States. We talked in English for about 20 minutes and then they suggested that I go upstairs and change into a suit. They advised that while eating dinner or conducting business, nobody in Warsaw gives anyone any respect unless they are wearing a dark suit and tie. They invited me . to join them for dinner as soon as I changed into appropriate attire. They said they would meet me in the hotel restaurant at 9:30. I returned to my room and changed into the single blue suit I had brought with me. After changing, I rejoined my new German friends just as they were moving toward the restaurant.

I'm glad I decided to join them. The place was full and those without reservations were turned away. The food was tasteless and we dubbed the main course "mystery meat." We made guesses as to what animal the meat came from. Even our waiter didn't know. We had him go to the kitchen to ask the chef what we were eating. His eventual reply was not very reassuring. In German he told my dinner partners, "The chef thinks it is beef." The Germans explained that this could either mean that the chef really didn't know what he was cooking, or he was too embarrassed to admit that this low cut of something was all the hotel had to serve. Almost all food was scarce in Poland in the 60s and the restaurant's patrons were glad to eat what was available.

I learned a lot from the Germans. They had been coming to Warsaw for several years. They told me that although there were no published or official restrictions on my traveling outside Warsaw, I should be careful: If I strayed too close to a military installation they would accuse me of espionage. They advised me to check my camera at the front desk when I left the hotel to travel beyond Warsaw city limits. Leaving it at the desk would keep it from being stolen and prevent the KGB from seizing it when I returned to the hotel. They told me horror stories of German tourists who had stopped to take photos of each other with some scenic Polish landscape in the background, only to be arrested because in the background of their snapshots, often miles away, were military structures. Once they had proved they were innocent tourists they were released, but sometimes that took weeks. I thanked them for the advice. They also told me that any English-speaking cab driver was a Polish government employee. This is why they said nothing when they entered the cab at the airport. Our driver, and all the rest of the cab drivers at the airport who spoke English, were low-level KGB agents whose main job was gathering information.

They told me to take the hotel address with me and show it to cab drivers when I wanted to return. I could have trouble getting back to the hotel without showing the address in Polish and most Polish citizens wouldn't help. The Warsaw residents are afraid of associating with people who speak English. They told me to always write down in Polish the address I wanted the cab to take me to, so there would be no mistake as to my destination. I asked the Germans about the truck that took our luggage at the airport and they said it was government policy. They have the right to search luggage, but seldom do. By taking it away from you at the airport, they more or less assure themselves that they could go through it for contraband if they wanted to. Since travelers don't know if their luggage will be searched, they are discouraged from trying to sneak in anything that is illegal to import. Mainly they look for U.S. cigarettes, alcohol, magazines and political propaganda that is contrary to Polish government policy. It was cheaper than a formal customs check. The luggage got to the hotel before we did because the cab driver is required to take a longer route.

The Germans warned me that many of the hotel clerks were KGB agents and that my room was probably bugged. If I wanted to make a phone call and not have it recorded, they suggested that I call from the U.S. Embassy, but even at the embassy there was no guarantee that the call would not be intercepted. The Germans were businessmen and very street smart. They gave me the name and address of a tourist shop that sold high-quality Polish crystal, exportable Polish antiques, and the only other exportable Polish tourist commodity, hand-carved, hand-painted wooden nesting dolls. They came in sets of up to 20 dolls of graduated size, with each smaller doll nesting inside the one that was slightly larger. The standard set was nine dolls. They are called "Matryoshki," which is a form of the word for mother. They told me to be careful of the black market, unless I went to "Praga." Apparently this one section of Warsaw was a totally free area where you could buy or sell anything and have no fear of being arrested. In Praga you could exchange foreign currency at the black market rate, buy drugs, or banned import items and sell anything of value that you brought from the United States.

The regular shopping area was called "Old Town," just across the square from the hotel. The prices were government regulated and were set up mainly for tourists. It was a crime to exchange money there for anything but the official rate of 17 zlotys to one U.S. dollar. The black market rate could be as high as 2,000 zlotys to one U.S. dollar. If you got caught illegally exchanging money, the KGB could seize all your money and immediately put you on the first available mode of transportation out of the country. If you ever came back and did it again, you would be sentenced to six months in a Polish jail. Unfortunately the jails were so unsanitary that even a sentence of a few months could be a death sentence. The only safe way to take advantage of the black market exchange rate was to exchange money or buy tourist goods using U.S. currency in Praga. The shopkeepers there would bargain on price if you paid in small denomination U.S. currency. Although you could not expect 2,000 to one exchange, you could get a lot better rate than the official rate of 17 to one.

I was impressed with how well my German companions could communicate with the Polish in German. They told me that all Polish children learn Russian and German because those countries share borders with Poland, and they are the countries that the Polish do most of their business with. I mentioned that I have considered taking German or French as a second language and almost in the same voice, they all said, "Don't be stupid, Graham, study English. That's the only language of the future." Now, whenever I am tempted to learn a foreign language, their words remind me that the entire world strives to communicate in English.

When we finished dinner, I said, "I guess we don't have to haggle over the dinner bill since meals are included in our hotel tab." In fact, all hotels behind the Iron Curtain are on the European plan, which means meals are included. The Germans were quick to point out that drinks are not included, and if I felt compelled to entertain them, we could retire to the lobby and I was more than welcome to buy them some after-dinner drinks.

While we were eating dinner, the main lobby of the hotel had been transformed into what could best be described as a dessert reception. There were trays of pastry, several types of coffee, and complimentary after-dinner 180 proof Polish vodka, laced with peppermint. Brandy and cognac were available at a slight charge. The scene was almost royal in its presentation: There were several men dressed in cutaway black coats with red sashes across their chests and a dozen or so medals pinned to their chests or on their coats. The Germans whispered that these men were retired Polish and Russian generals who stopped in at the Bristol every night for the free vodka. The hotel tolerated them because their colorful uniforms gave the hotel some much-needed class.

The Germans all wanted brandy, and I bought them a bottle of V.S.O.P. that they finished in about 20 minutes. I was enjoying the high-proof peppermint vodka, but soon we all were sleepy and one by one we headed for our rooms.

I bade farewell to my German friends and went to my room, my head pounding from the high-alcohol vodka I had consumed. Our hall steward was taking suits and shoes out of the door cabinets of the rooms on my floor. I saw my neighbor across the hall place his suit and shirt into the wardrobe and lock it with his room key. I undressed and put my shoes, blue suit and white shirt in the wardrobe inside my door. I also hung the slacks and shirt I wore on the plane in the wardrobe. There was a small sack for laundry in the bottom of the wardrobe. I filled it with all the underclothes that needed to be washed and used my room key to lock the cabinet.

I turned on the small radio on the nightstand. There was only one station. It played symphony music by Polish and Russian composers. It was pleasant at first but soon became monotonous. Every so often the announcer would speak a few words in Polish and then another symphony would start. Tchaikovsky was, of course, their favorite. It put me right to sleep. I woke up in the middle of the night and they were playing the same piece of Tchaikovsky music that I had fallen asleep to. I turned off the radio assured that any music I missed could be heard later.

I slept well, and in the morning the first thing I did was check to see what had happened to my shoes and clothes. The shoes were shined, right where I left them. Both shirts were laundered and my suit was nicely pressed. They even ironed my socks and underwear. I found out later that there was no charge for this service and when I tried to tip my steward, I was advised that tipping was not allowed. I tipped him anyway, with a Kennedy half dollar and some of the Marlboro cigarettes I bought in the duty-free shop on my SAS flight. He accepted the tip graciously and almost as if it was expected. I sensed that these stewards were not supposed to accept tips but if anyone persisted, they were quick to break the no tipping rule. He looked up and down the hall each way before he stuffed the Marlboro boxes and the coin in his coat. The tip was a mistake; every time I saw the steward after that, he wanted more of whatever he could get out of me. He became a pest that I had to deal with every time I entered or left my room. I learned a valuable lesson on tipping. The tipper should withhold tipping until the last day to avoid being pestered by the person being tipped.

I dressed in my newly pressed white shirt and dark blue suit and looked out my window. It was a bright and sunny day. The muted noise of the city could be heard through the glass in my window. It was coming from the square below. There were thousands of people, many on bicycles. There were only a few cars and none of them U.S. models. There were some Mercedes sedans and BMWs that I recognized, but the rest were cars I had never seen before. Some were small and emitted a lot of smoke from their exhaust, and some were very large and looked like limousines from the 1930s. I have been in love with every form of automobile since I was a toddler. One of the anticipated highlights of coming to Europe was that I expected to see exotic European cars that were rare in Seattle. In Warsaw, there were hardly any cars, let alone exotic ones.

I left the hotel, armed with the address of the U.S.

Embassy on a slip of paper. I hailed a cab and showed the driver the address. He responded in English that he knew the way. I thought to myself, "Of course you do. It was taught to you in your KGB training." We passed several of the huge sedans that looked exactly like 1930-1938 Packard limousines and I asked the driver where they were made and how old they were. He told me they were current models made in Russia.

They came in only three models. The largest was a Zim, with the Zis or Zil sedans slightly smaller. He said, "They are the best cars in the world and only very important people are allowed to ride in them." I snickered at his misguided admiration for these antique tanks that looked like gangster cars out of a 1930 mobster movie. They looked about as easy to drive as a U.S. Army Dodge Power Wagon. They were driven by chauffeurs with nobody in the passenger seat. The Zims were easy to recognize as they were longer with two seats in the rear. There was usually only one passenger in the rear seat of the Zis or Zil sedans but several of the larger Zims had as many as four passengers in the back. We drove along in silence and as we got closer to the embassies, there were more and more of the big cars and fewer of the little ones.

The neighborhood gradually changed from the type of buildings near the center of town to large and quite beautiful homes. This was obviously where the wealthy families of Warsaw lived. The beautiful homes suddenly stopped as we approached a cluster of elegant brick and cement buildings that my driver announced as "Embassy Row."

As we approached the embassies my driver said, "You are seeing one of the largest concentration of Zims in Poland as nearly all the important diplomats consider it the only car to drive in Warsaw." I saw more cars in the few blocks surrounding the embassies than I had in all of downtown Warsaw. The parking lots leading up to the embassy area were full, and many of the cars in them were the small ones that I saw emitting smoke near the square. The cab driver was correct about the number of Zims. There was row after row of the large black Zims in the front of the parking lots and in the driveways of the embassies.

The embassies were all in the space of a few blocks. The buildings themselves were of varied architecture. Most were three to four stories high and appeared to be several hundred years old. I learned later that they all had been built in the last 15 years. My driver slowed down and said, "Here we are at the U.S. Embassy."

I was disappointed as I stared at the ultra-modern five-story glass and concrete structure that my country had built right in the middle of all the beautiful brick buildings. It stuck out like a sore thumb. It belonged in Los Angeles, not Embassy Row in Warsaw. It was by far the tallest and biggest embassy in Warsaw. The early morning sunlight bounced off the glass walls like a blinding searchlight. There were armed U.S. Marines standing near the front entrance. In front of the building was an asphalt parking lot that was full of large Mercedes sedans. There were a few BMWs and even some luxury U.S. cars. I was particularly impressed with a current model year Cadillac limousine with two small American flags on small staffs on the front fenders that was parked just to the right of the front entrance. I surmised that it was the American ambassadors car.

I paid the cab driver, exited the cab and walked toward the main entrance.

Warsaw United States Embassy

CHAPTER ELEVEN

THE U.S. EMBASSY IN POLAND

As I approached the entrance, a young clean-shaven U.S. Marine in dress uniform stopped me and politely asked for my identification. When he saw I was an American citizen he waved me past his checkpoint. I walked in the large front entrance and was faced with a mob of about 150 people trying to get past a second check-point, also manned by U.S. Marine guards. They were stationed at a narrowed passageway a dozen or so yards from the main reception area. I needed access to the offices behind the Marines, so I waded into the crowd. Without my passport it was hard to prove my identity. I gave the first Marine I talked to my business card showing that I was a lawyer from the United States. He ushered me right through the crowd. I went upstairs to a small reception desk. I was about the tenth person in line, and after an hour wait, I met with a junior embassy officer and told him why I was in Poland.

I asked for advice on the best method of traveling to Southern Poland without getting into trouble. He asked me to return to the waiting area and he would get me an answer. About 15 minutes later I was directed to a much larger office where I was introduced to a senior embassy officer who was willing to discuss my mission with me. Clarence Clemshaw was a career Foreign Service diplomat. He was dressed in a gray flannel suit and looked very distinguished. He was about 6 feet tall, with a slim build and a full head of silver-gray hair. He reminded me of Spencer Tracy, the famous movie star.

He was glad to talk with me about anything except traveling in Poland. He even asked me to join him and his wife for dinner that evening. His wife attended the University of Washington, my alma mater. He said she would love to hear about what was going on in Seattle. He had served in London, Paris, Berlin, Rome and now Warsaw. He said that the crowds of people in the main entrance were always there. They were Polish nationals, claiming to have U.S. relatives, trying to get visas to travel to the United States. He said, "Every time we grant a visa, there is a 95% chance that the person will travel to the United States, get lost in the Polish community of Chicago or New York, and never come back to Poland. The embassy adopted a policy of treating the visa requests as immigration applications, because that's what they were as a practical matter."

He went on to explain that the U.S. government couldn't stop the visa application process so the policy was to slow it down. Most of the Polish citizens wanting to come to the United States as permanent residents had no vocational skills that would make them eligible for normal immigration. They know this, so they apply for tourist visas to get around the rules and across the border. Once in the U.S. they go into hiding as soon as their tourist visa expires. The embassy had just one visa application clerk and she worked as slowly as she could processing all the requests.

He discussed the gaudy glass and steel embassy building and made excuses for the structure not blending into the other historic buildings in the area. For several years after World War II, the United States occupied older buildings that looked like the other embassies in Warsaw. After a few years the embassy staff found that every room was bugged with sophisticated listening devices. Their solution was to tear down the old embassy and build a modern building that couldn't be bugged. They did that in the early 60s but soon found that the new embassy contained more listening devices than the old embassy. It was built with Polish labor and many of the workers worked for the KGB. I asked what our country was going to do and he said, "We plan to tear down this building in the next year or two and rebuild it with imported U.S. labor. We own this property and the general feeling is that it is so flawed with clandestine listening devices, the only way to make it secure is to tear it down and start over."

Clarence said that discussions with any degree of classification were conducted in "safe" rooms. They were small, lead-shielded rooms in the bowels of the embassy. They were swept constantly and still were not considered foolproof. These rooms were scheduled for use weeks in advance and he was therefore unwilling to discuss what I was doing in Poland unless we had access to a safe room. I started to say that my trip to Warsaw was not a classified matter. He put his finger to his lips in a shushing pose and scribbled something on his note pad. He slid the pad over to me and said, "Thank you for stopping by." He got up and left the room. The note he gave me said, "Save your conversation for dinner. We will be in front of your hotel at 7 p.m. sharp." I left the embassy and caught a cab back to the hotel. The driver spoke only Polish and he stopped to show a traffic cop the card with the hotel's address on it. Apparently he couldn't read. I was lucky to get back to the hotel in one piece as my driver sipped cheap vodka most of the way, failed to stop at four stop signs, and hit several curbs. I tipped him a few zloty and left him fumbling with the money I gave him.

I had about five hours before I met Clarence and his wife for dinner. I decided to cross the square into the "Old Town" shopping area that the Germans had told me about. Old Town was built after the war. It was constructed from old brick and stone and appeared to be several hundred years older than it really is. The Polish government controls the prices the merchants charge in an attempt to capture as many tourist dollars as possible. Price control usually means putting a ceiling on what can be charged, but in Warsaw it is a price floor that the shop owners cannot undercut. I was sure the prices were better in "Praga" but even the tourist guidebooks say that the charm of Old

Town shouldn't be missed on a trip to Warsaw. Just don't buy the high-priced goods for sale. With a firm grip on my wallet I headed for Old Town.

Warsaw Tourist Carriage
in the Market Square

The Old Town Market Square, Warsaw

CHAPTER TWELVE

OLD TOWN

It It was a short walk across the square. I passed a huge building that looked like the Lincoln Memorial in Washington, D.C., without Lincoln in it. It was white marble and granite and appeared to be the centerpiece of the square. It was the Warsaw Opera House. It was easily the length of several football fields and about six stories high. The current production was the opera, "Aida." I decided to see if I could get a ticket, but the box office was closed and had a sign in Polish that obviously meant "sold out."

Off to the side of the Opera House was a war memorial that was quite spectacular. It was nearly as tall as the Opera House and about 300 feet wide. The memorial showed a group of Polish soldiers defending a high piece of terrain against the Germans. There were thousands of names engraved on the memorial. At the top there was a black bird in flight that could have been a raven or a hawk. I was puzzled over why it was there. There were a few flowers at the base, and several families were there, paying their respects. It was a somber scene and I didn't stay long.

I headed to the other side of the square toward Old

Town, where the Germans had said I'd find the tourist shops. I entered a very narrow street, too narrow for trucks of any size; even a small car would not have had much room to pass. The buildings looked several hundred years old and they housed numerous quaint antique and crystal shops. I visited the glass shops first and found them to be stocked with beautiful cut crystal plates, vases and glasses of every kind and description. I went to the next store and their stock was identical to the first shop. The prices were the same. I decided to see if I could bargain with the shop-keeper of the second shop. Using the 500-1 multiple that the Germans suggested, I tried to buy a set of glassware and a 2-foot-high flower vase for my mother.

The sales clerk not only refused, but she appeared to be frightened by my offer. I got the same result at every shop in Old Town when I tried to haggle over the posted price. The glassware was still cheap at the 17-1 exchange rate, but I decided not to buy it, partly because of the lack of bargaining with the shopkeepers and partly because I was reluctant to carry so much weight in cut glass with me. The antique shops gave me a similar reception. I decided to go back to the hotel and leave shopping for another day. I was still experiencing some jet lag and the prospect of a two-hour nap sounded pretty good to me after walking around Warsaw for several hours.

On the way across the square I was approached by a man dressed in soiled and torn clothes. He looked like one of the typical panhandlers that hang out in city parks in the

United States. He confronted me with a large roll of zlotys and asked in broken English, "Do you want to trade zlotys for U.S. dollars?" I instantly said no. He persisted, offering me 500 zloty to one if I could exchange at least $100 in U.S. currency. I again declined. His next offer was 1000 to 1. I turned my back on him and walked away. As I neared the southern edge of the square he said, in perfect English "Fifteen-hundred to one is my last offer." I stepped off the curb and headed toward the hotel without answering or looking back.

He cursed me in mixed English and Polish as the distance between us widened. There was a policeman by the hotel. I went over to him and complained about the man harassing me. He looked in the direction of the departing man and said, also in perfect English, "I can't leave my post to arrest a beggar." The English was the clue that they were both KGB agents. I guess the money exchanger had targeted me as someone with U.S. dollars after I tried to bargain with the shopkeepers in Old Town. I am sure he thought that I would exchange dollars for zloty at close to the black market rate, and then he could make me give up all my dollars to avoid being arrested for money changing. My German friends had warned me that low-level KGB agents strip tourists of their cash in exchange for not reporting them for petty money exchange violations. My dinner with the Germans was already paying dividends.

I went in a side door of the hotel and as I went past

the front desk I noticed that it was empty. I went straight to my room and got there just as the cleaning staff was leaving. There was a loud buzzing noise coming from my bedside radio. I thought the maid had left it on, but when I got closer I saw that it was off: the dial was not lit. Remembering my conversation with my German friends about the room being bugged, on a hunch, I put my head down low to the radio speaker and yelled in a loud voice, "I'm back." The radio buzz was instantly reduced as if someone had suddenly turned down the volume.

The radio was not an effective listening device. All I had to do was turn it on and the symphony music would drown out any sounds made in the room. I decided they used it to know when I entered and left my room.

I put my blue suit and shirt in the door closet and my shoes on the door closet shelf. I summoned my room steward, gave him a pack of cigarettes, and asked him to get my clothes back in my door closet by 6:30 p.m. He nodded and said, "Yes, sir. I will have them done for you immediately." I called the front desk and asked for a 6:30 wake-up call. I turned on the radio and lay down on the bed for a nap. I fell asleep in an instant. Tchaikovsky playing softly is better than a sleeping pill. Maybe that's why they play it so often. It's healthier than vodka.

My phone rang at 6:30 on the dot. The desk clerk asked if I would need an early dinner reservation, and I replied that I was going out. I checked my door closet and my shirt and suit were there, all properly cleaned and pressed, and my shoes had been shined. After I showered, shaved and dressed, I went through my legal documents so that dates and events would be fresh in my mind when I had dinner with the Clemshaws. I left the room and headed for the hotel's front steps. It was just before 7:00 p.m.

The Clemshaw's 300 SEL

CHAPTER THIRTEEN

THE CLEMSHAWS

A dark Mercedes 300 SEL was waiting at the curb. Clarence and a woman I took to be his wife were in the back seat. A uniformed driver jumped out and opened the back door for me, and Clarence introduced me to his wife Mary. The driver put the car in gear and we headed north out of the city. Before long the buildings of Warsaw gave way to rolling fields and lush forests. The countryside was a lot like the Pacific Northwest.

I asked where we were going and Clarence indicated that we were headed toward a beautiful lake near Serok, a small town just northwest of Warsaw. There were very few cars on the road; the Polish residents we saw were mainly on foot. It was early May, but still light at 7 p.m. Our car was the subject of intense interest to the evening strollers. As the large, black Mercedes sped along the highway at 50 mph, the people on the side of the road stepped off the highway and stared in awe as we sped past. Several small children waved, but their accompanying parents showed no emotion as we drove by. At first, the attention made me feel like a celebrity. Soon, I felt less like a celebrity and more like a powerful dictator of a police state. We were being tolerated by the people we passed. Poland in the spring of 1967 was not a happy country.

After about an hour, we arrived at a log and stucco structure on the edge of a beautiful lake. The lake was deep blue and the lodge with its rustic logs blended into the tall trees around the lake. It looked more like a hunting lodge in Idaho than a restaurant in Poland. There were several BMWs in the parking lot and two of the big Russian Zims. We were greeted at the door by a cheerful woman in her mid 40s who seemed to know Clarence and his wife. She guided us to a table facing the lake with a beautiful view of the surrounding area. We saw several small boats off in the distance with two or three fishermen casting lines out into the deep blue waters. There were two small sailboats headed away from us that were heeled over and running fast in the evening breeze.

As we entered the lodge, Clarence nodded to guests at several tables as we passed. It was a very pleasant place, and everyone seemed to be having a good time. The long drawn faces I witnessed at dinner in Warsaw were replaced by happy patrons conversing over cocktails or dinner. I noticed that Mary was the only woman in the restaurant except for our hostess. All the men were dressed in suits and everyone was drinking vodka.

The absence of any wine on the menu startled me. I thought that a restaurant of this caliber must serve wine. I asked Clarence and he remarked that almost all wine in Poland is imported, and it costs about three times what a bottle of vodka costs. He said that the tourist restaurants in Warsaw carry wine, but it is seldom seen in the rural restaurants. Clarence suggested that I order fish; he readily conceded that meat was an unknown commodity in Poland and to be avoided. Fish on the other hand was local and well prepared. Mary and I let him order for us. Shortly, a basket of bread, a bowl of caviar, and a bottle of vodka were brought to the table. The vodka was served in a beautiful crystal decanter similar to the ones I saw in the glass shops by the square. Clarence remarked that the vodka was at least 100 proof and so smooth that it was easy to drink straight. It was also easy to drink too much. The local vodka in Poland was one of its least known valuable resources in 1967.

The food arrived and it turned out to be a three-course fish dinner. The first course was a small fresh water crayfish that they called lobster. It was good, but definitely not lobster. The second course was a pink fish similar in flavor to salmon but richer. It was more like a Northwest steelhead trout. Clarence explained that it was local sturgeon. The last course was a very delicate white fish that I thought to be sole. Clarence told me that the Polish pride themselves in the preparation of this fish. It was called Polish pike perch which was like sole but somewhat more firm. It was simmered in white wine with black pepper and bay leaf. They served selected vegetables with each course. There were small tender new red potatoes with the shellfish course, a very delicate white asparagus, that was huge by our standards, with the sturgeon, and some sliced pickled beets with the pike perch. By the time we were ready for dessert, Mary and I were protesting that we were too full. Clarence summoned the woman that originally greeted us and told her in Polish that his guests were not going to have dessert. Our host refused to take no for an answer and returned, pushing a cart with a small butane cook stove on it. She skillfully prepared a crepe with a cherry sauce that was too good to pass up.

Clarence avoided talking about anything concerning his business or my mission during dinner. Each time I started to discuss Stanislaw's estate, he put up his hand in a defensive manner, clearly indicating that this was not the right time. After dinner we went for a stroll by the lake. Clarence whispered that it was fine to talk now. I walked between Mary and Clarence and told them how my efforts to locate Stanislaw's missing relatives were being thwarted at every turn. They offered little advice and indicated that my story was one they had heard a hundred times before. Poland was so devastated after two World Wars that the survivors kept to themselves. They wanted no outside interference with their lives and were very secretive about everything they did.

Clarence told me that he and his family enjoyed diplomatic immunity and were free to travel anywhere in Poland. They spent some time traveling around the countryside when they first arrived, but now they stick pretty close to Warsaw and the comforts of the American embassy. The diplomatic social life was exhausting for both of them. There were 29 foreign embassies in Warsaw, and each had important governmental visitors each month from their respective countries. Barely a day went by without an invitation to attend a reception and dinner at one of the neighboring embassies.

Then Clarence told me the real reason we were having dinner. Mary wanted to hear the latest news about her favorite place in the world, Seattle, Washington. The next hour was devoted to telling Mary what had happened in Seattle since she left in the early' 50s. I told her all about the recent World's Fair: the new monorail that serviced downtown Seattle, and the new Space Needle that towered over the Seattle skyline. She had seen it all in Elvis Presley's movie, "It Happened at the World's Fair," but still wanted to hear more about it, firsthand. I told her about the new buildings in downtown Seattle and the new floating bridge to Bellevue over Lake Washington. I was even able to tell her of the medical advances coming out of the bone marrow transplant operations that were occurring at the hospital I worked for. I was the attorney for Swedish Hospital in Seattle who helped found the Hutchinson Cancer Research Center next to our main building. She was shocked to hear that Seattle doctors were curing leukemia for patients from all over the world. We talked about my work at Swedish Hospital for over an hour.

Finally, I got them back to discussing my reason for coming to Poland. I explained that in my heir search I had identified a town, "Pionki," which I had found on a map of Poland. It was about 100 miles southeast of Warsaw. Lanski was supposed to be near Pionki. Clarence said I could spend the rest of my life searching for Lanski, and I would get no help from Polish citizens: No one wants to be involved with Americans. Poland was behind the Iron Curtain. Any Polish citizen that fraternized with Western foreigners was investigated for espionage by the KGB. He said my only chance was to get a trustworthy interpreter and driver and go to Pionki and ask for directions to Lanski. He said I might get lucky. I asked if he could help me find an off-duty U.S. embassy employee who could help, and he told me it was impossible. Any Polish national who worked for the embassy and took a job outside of the embassy would be fired. It was against regulations for a diplomat or embassy employee to take money for outside employment. He said, "You don't have enough money with you for one of the embassy employees to take the risk."

I asked if it made any sense to check the local Catholic Church for Stocowski records as my deceased client's family was Catholic. Clarence said, "The Catholic church had been driven underground. The existing church structures around Poland are mainly symbolic of better times." He doubted that any Catholic records existed. I was about ready to pack my bags and head for home when I remembered my meeting with Dr. Marion Zeiss. That memory changed our conversation for the rest of the evening and became the start of my solution to the Stocowski estate dilemma.

The Lodge By The Lake

Warsaw Patriots Memorial

CHAPTER FOURTEEN

DR. ZEISS

I asked Clarence and his wife if they had ever heard of a Dr. Marion Zeiss. They both looked at me wide eyed and in one voice said, "Who hasn't." To my shock and delight, I learned that he was one of the most famous living Polish heroes. He was one of a handful of Polish citizens who could come and go from Poland and do pretty much whatever he wanted. He was a wearer of the "Black Raven" and one of the few surviving World War II Polish Patriots. I remembered seeing a black raven over the war memorial in the square and I asked what it meant. They explained that when the Germans retreated from Warsaw in July 1944, 30,000 Polish underground patriots came out of hiding and tried to prevent the retreating Germans from burning and looting Warsaw as they withdrew.

The patriots used bullets and gasoline they had saved for years. They torched the German tanks and shot German soldiers as they were desperately trying to escape. This handful of patriots was successful in destroying the German occupying force and saving the city from ruin. Soon a huge Russian army arrived at the eastern outskirts of Warsaw and set up camp on the east bank of the Vistula

River. Marion Zeiss, a general in the Polish army, took his regiment of patriots across the river with wagonloads of vodka to greet the Russian army. For three days the Polish and Russians celebrated the rescue of Warsaw.

The Polish had captured several hundred German SS Nazi officers, and they marched them across the river to impress the Russians. The Russians showed the Polish how they dealt with a defeated enemy. The German officers were stripped naked. Some were tortured before they were set on fire or beheaded. Their naked bodies, many burned beyond recognition, or headless, were hung by their feet from any pole or building near the bridge. These SS officers were the worst and most sadistic of the Germans who occupied Russia and Poland. The swift punishment to them by the Russian soldiers was retribution for the years of suffering that SS Nazi officers had inflicted on the citizens of their homeland.

Over a thousand Polish women had consorted with the enemy. Those who were caught were shaved bald, raped by the Russian soldiers and stoned to death by the Warsaw residents. What was left of the Warsaw ghetto was liberated and the few surviving Jews began long pilgrimages to wherever they had come from.

A large group of Russian officers came into Warsaw and were entertained in royal fashion. Food and vodka hoarded for years magically appeared and the celebration continued. When the celebration was over, the Russians stayed right where they were on the east bank of the Vistula

River on Stalin's orders. It was a short-lived celebration. Hitler was incensed that the Russians and Poles had the audacity to kill, burn and behead his SS Nazi officers. The fact that their naked corpses were hung upside down from Warsaw's light poles sent Hitler into an uncontrollable rage.

Against the advice of his remaining military staff, Hitler diverted a previously unused Panzer division to Poland, a division that had been held in reserve to protect Berlin. Hitler ordered them to destroy Warsaw. The Panzer tank division traveled the 300 miles in less than two days, and when the Polish army saw them enter the western out-skirts of Warsaw, General Zeiss urged the Russians to cross the river and help the Polish army defend the city. The Russians refused to help. They didn't even offer the Polish army supplies or ammunition.

As the German tanks entered Warsaw from the west, destroying everything in their paths, General Zeiss mus-tered his remaining men, and in a dash to the Warsaw city offices rescued the plans and architectural drawings of the city. He found a safe place to hide them and then he and the Polish army fought a vicious hand-to-hand, street-by-street battle to save Warsaw. Their effort was in vain. Their small "Molotov cocktails" could not compete with a well-supplied Panzer division.

The Russians turned from saviors to spoilers and patiently waited while the Germans destroyed every building in Warsaw. This was one of the biggest mistakes of Hitler's futile war. Gas and ammunition for the defense of Berlin were wasted in spiteful revenge against Poland and Russia for daring to kill the German SS Nazi officers.

Russia has claimed that the sacrificing of Warsaw was necessary to deplete Hitler's reserves before the Russian army attacked Germany from the east. This was a lame excuse. The real reason was that Stalin had great plans for his new Polish Empire. A victorious Polish army would have given him an obstacle of national pride that would have made Soviet occupation of Poland very difficult. By letting Hitler vent his wrath on Warsaw, Stalin succeeded in depleting the German reserves and destroying the remains of the Polish army without firing a single Russian bullet.

When the attack was over, the magnificent history of Warsaw had disappeared in a pile of rubble. No building in the heart of Warsaw for three square miles was left standing. The Panzer division collected their dead, rescued some low ranking German soldiers who had been imprisoned by the Poles in makeshift POW camps, and left as quickly as they had come.

General Zeiss and fewer than 300 Polish soldiers survived. The Russians came into the city and began their occupation of Poland with no opposition. The Russians in charge decreed that the city of Warsaw was to be relocated. General Zeiss and the others pledged cooperation if the Russians would rebuild Warsaw exactly as it was before it was razed by the Germans. He had the old city plans. The

Russians agreed; It gave the Poles something to do. The city was rebuilt just as it had been. Where streets were 12 feet wide, they were rebuilt exactly 12 feet wide. The builders used old pictures showing placement of trees and other landscaping to replant the city just as it was before it was destroyed. The construction teams scoured the old plans and pictures to ensure that everything was rebuilt from the same materials that were originally used. Clarence said that all the historic buildings in the center of Warsaw are less than 20 years old.

The Polish patriots adopted the raven as their recognition sign much the same as the early Christians adopted the sign of a fish as theirs. The raven sign is a medal of honor to the Polish.

In Seattle, I met Marion Zeiss as a world-famous orthopedic surgeon. My discovery that he was a general in the Polish army put him in an entirely different light. I learned from Clarence that Marion Zeiss went to Russia after the war to study medicine. He did his residency in orthopedic surgery at a large Moscow hospital. He came to Warsaw, started an orthopedic service at Warsaw's largest hospital, and was so successful that the hospital became the largest orthopedic hospital behind the Iron Curtain. Dr. Zeiss was one of the most popular leaders in Poland, and Clarence and Mary both wanted to know how I knew him. I told them about our chance meeting at a Seattle lawn party and mentioned that he gave me a private unlisted phone number to contact him when I got to Warsaw. They both encouraged me to follow up by contacting Dr. Zeiss. Clarence was particularly interested in Dr. Zeiss' brother who worked for the Polish government in the "Missing Persons" office. He said, "The embassy has been trying to learn the names of the Polish government workers in that office for a long time. Any information that you could provide us would be greatly appreciated." I suddenly became very uncomfortable and began to question the Clemshaws' motives for inviting me to dinner.

I sensed from my army intelligence training that Clarence was interested in developing Marion Zeiss and his brother into sources of information. I remembered the lecture from intelligence school that taught us, "New informants are the primary tool of all intelligence agencies." I quietly promised myself that I would not help the U.S. embassy use Dr. Zeiss or his brother. I had little to gain and risked being accused of espionage if Dr. Zeiss or his brother sensed that they were being used as an information source for the United States. Either of them could report me to the KGB and I, unlike the Clemshaws, had no diplomatic immunity. As quickly as those thoughts surfaced, they evaporated. The Clemshaws had just bought me a very nice dinner and we were enjoying a lovely spring evening in the suburbs of Warsaw. I also reasoned that the least I could do was to keep the embassy informed of my progress as long as they were offering their assistance in finding the Stocowski heirs.

I decided to call Dr. Zeiss first thing in the morning.

Clarence, Mary and I were all tired, and as we finished our walk and got back in the Mercedes for the ride into town, I could barely keep my eyes open. Mary was sound asleep when we pulled up in front of the Bristol Hotel. I thanked Clarence for the lovely evening and promised to give him a report before I left Poland. I waved at the hotel doorman and headed into the hotel. When I got to my room the familiar buzz was on the radio. As I got closer to the night-stand I heard the volume of the buzz turned down. At least someone in Warsaw was interested in my activity.

I put my clothes and shoes in the wardrobe and jumped in bed. I was sound asleep in less than five minutes.

Bristol Hotel

CHAPTER FIFTEEN

CONTACT WITH DR. ZEISS

Since I had been warned that the hotel phones might be bugged, I was reluctant to use the one in my room to call Dr. Zeiss. I thought of neighboring businesses that might let me borrow a phone for a private call. The LOT ticket office was a few doors south of the hotel. Since I needed a flight schedule to plan for my return to the West I thought this would be a good excuse to go to the office and then ask to use their phone. When I got to the office, I picked up a schedule and casually asked the woman at the counter if I could use her phone to confirm a luncheon date. She smiled and handed me her phone, reversing it so that the phone dial was facing me. I took out the number Dr. Zeiss had given me and dialed.

The phone call was answered in Polish. I hesitated and than asked for Dr. Zeiss in English. The person that answered said, "Please to hold." After about 30 seconds a woman came on the line and said in perfect English, "Can I help you?" I asked to speak to Dr. Zeiss and was told that he was in surgery all day and that it was impossible to talk with him. Then the woman asked who I was and what I wanted. I explained that I met Dr. Zeiss in Seattle and was visiting Warsaw on business. I told her that I had some gifts for Dr. Zeiss. She said, "One moment, please." After a five-minute wait, a loud male voice came on the line and gruffly said, "Who is this?" I said, "I am Graham Taylor, a lawyer from Seattle. Is this Dr. Zeiss?" The answer was "Yes."

Our conversation was very short. Dr. Zeiss remembered who I was and said he would see me later in the day. He told me to stand next to the Chopin Memorial in Lazienki Park at 4:30. He would send someone to pick me up. I started to thank him, but he hung up.

The park was easy to find. It was several blocks from the hotel and within walking distance. I was standing in front of the Chopin Memorial at precisely 4:30. I brought a carton of cigarettes, two bottles of Jim Beam, a bottle of Crown Royal and several rolls of Kennedy half-dollars. Suddenly a Zim traveling at a high rate of speed appeared to my right and screeched to a stop. A voice commanded, "Get in." I bent over to look inside and there was a young man I had never seen before in a doctor's green operating smock. The smock was covered with fresh blood. I got in and introduced myself. His name was Klaus and he was a resident at Dr. Zeiss' hospital. As the Zim sped away, he said that Dr. Zeiss was finishing up some surgery and that he had asked Klaus to pick me up and bring me back to the hospital. He drove fast but with precise skill. Within a few minutes we arrived at the hospital and stopped at a guarded steel gate. An armed military guard waived us through.

The building we approached looked more like a prison than a hospital. For a panicked moment I wondered whether I had fallen into a KGB trap. I looked around frantically for something familiar to a hospital and then I spotted ambulances by what appeared to be an emergency entrance. I let out a sigh of relief; It really was a hospital.

The huge, stark building was made of dark granite blocks. It was four stories tall and stretched for a quarter of a mile. It was a gigantic gray rectangular block of stone with tiny windows on each floor. There were bars on the windows on the lower floors.

We drove into a basement garage. Klaus steered the big Zim into a reserved parking stall. He got out and I followed. We entered an elevator and went up two floors. When I exited the elevator, I found myself in the middle of a circle of operating rooms. Klaus threw me a green surgical gown, a mask and a small green paper hat. He said, "Get scrubbed over there," pointing to a small sink. "Join us in operating room four as soon as you can." He seemed to think I knew what to do. Fortunately, a young intern or resident was scrubbing for surgery at the next sink. I watched his movements and committed them to memory. Near the sink were lockers and a bench. I put my coat and briefcase and the sack of gifts for Dr. Zeiss in an empty locker. I turned the key I found in the locker door and put it in my pocket. My briefcase had a lot of cash in it, but I had no choice. I pulled on the loose-fitting green surgical pants and smock and put the paper hat on my head. It had an elastic band and fit snugly. I went to the sink and scrubbed my hands and forearms as I had seen the young doctor do before me. When I was through, a nurse appeared and motioned for me to put my hands up. She stretched rubber gloves over my hands and motioned for me to go into operating room four.

When I walked in, there was an operation in progress, and several people in surgical gowns were working frantically around the operating table. Dr. Zeiss was among them. In a booming voice he said, "Welcome, Graham. Nice to see you again. Come over here and help." He spoke to the rest of his staff at the operating table in Polish. It was plain that he was introducing me as Dr. Taylor from Seattle. For a minute or two, I thought Dr. Zeiss had me confused with one of the orthopedic surgeons he had met in Seattle, but then he winked at me. He was just having a little fun with me and his staff.

When I looked at the patient on the operating table I realized that Dr. Zeiss was sawing off a man's right leg, just below the knee. I could see that the foot was badly smashed as if it had been run over by a train or heavy truck. I have never been squeamish, and the sight of the blood didn't bother me until Dr. Zeiss handed me the saw and said, "Would you finish up?" I must have turned green because he laughed out loud and finished the job himself. He threw the man's foot toward the door, but before it hit the floor, an orderly stepped out of the shadows, caught it and placed it on a table at the edge of the room. The toss and catch was like a good pass in basketball: This maneuver had been done many times before. Next while the residents clamped off bleeders in the stump, Dr. Zeiss took a 6-inch stainless steel rod and attached it to the remaining portion of the patient's tibia. The implant was hollow at one end and was obviously custom made to fit this patient. It slipped over the exposed bone so tightly that the doctors had to pound it on with a hammer. When the rod was in place, Dr. Zeiss took four stainless steel screws, and through four small holes in the hollow end of the implant, fastened them through the implant into the bone. He used an electric drill that looked like the one I had on my workbench at home. When the screws were in place, he took off his mask, his hat and his right glove and extended his hand to me and said, "Welcome to Warsaw, Graham." He gave me a bear hug and, with his arm around me, said, "Let me show you my hospital." We left the operating room and headed down the hall. Everywhere we went, the employees stepped aside and more or less hugged the walls to let us pass. They were not afraid of him, it was more a sign of their admiration of their leader. We went in room after room and visited patients on whom Dr. Zeiss had recently operated. Most of them were amputees and most had had lower limbs replaced with artificial implants. After visiting a dozen patients we stopped at a water cooler for a cup of water. He told me he performed 80 to 125 surgeries every month. This was far fewer than just after the war when there were more than a million men from Poland and

Russia who required arms or legs surgically corrected or removed. He said, "The lucky ones came to my hospital." Modesty was not one of Dr. Ziess' personality traits. There were about 600 beds in the hospital and they were all full. When I tried to talk about my mission in Poland, he cautioned me to wait until later.

After completing rounds and a tour of the hospital, we went to the recovery room to check on the patient whose foot had just been amputated. The anesthetic was just beginning to wear off, and he was trying to sit up and look at the spot where his foot used to be. An artificial foot was already being attached to the stainless steel implant protruding through the plastic cap that had been fitted over the bandages covering his stump. Dr. Zeiss patted the patient on the back and told him in English, "The surgery was perfect." He introduced me as Dr. Taylor who had come from Seattle to help him with the difficult surgery he had performed. The patient thanked me in English although he had a heavy German accent. As we left, Dr. Zeiss told me the man was an East German army officer who had his foot run over by a tank at an East Berlin checkpoint. This hospital was a collection depot for all of the eastern block's orthopedic injuries. Dr. Zeiss said that the officer would be walking on the new foot tonight and that he would be back at work within two weeks. This was the orthopedic wave of the future: Early release and fast recovery.

Dr. Zeiss was very proud of his operating rooms. He

had arranged five operating rooms radiating from a small circle so that he could quickly go from room to room by passing through the hub or center of the circle. Dr. Zeiss said that surgeons came from all over the world to learn his techniques. He was glad to share knowledge and train the visiting doctors so long as they used genuine Zeissimer stainless steel prostheses in their work when they returned to wherever they had come from. Dr. Zeiss said that he owned the company that made the prostheses and even though they were very expensive, he tried to supply them at cost to western orthopedic hospitals and physicians. He winked at me and made it very obvious that he made a handsome profit on every stainless steel implant that he sold.

When we finished making rounds, Dr. Zeiss told me to collect my belongings and go down one floor, turn left and go to the northwest corner of the building. I went back to the locker and retrieved my belongings. I threw the green surgical gown in a hamper and left the locker key in the door where I found it. I went down one floor and walked down a dimly lit hall toward the northwest corner of the building. As I neared the end of the corridor I saw a glass-paneled door different from the other solid wood doors on the floor. I looked inside and saw a beautiful woman sitting at a reception desk in front of a door that had Dr. Zeiss' name on it. She was in her late 20s and as good looking as Grace Kelly at that age. I went inside and introduced myself. The woman stood up and, with a smile that would melt an iceberg, grasped my outstretched hand in both of hers and said in perfect English, "Hi, you must be Mr. Taylor. I'm Monica, Dr. Zeiss' personal assistant. Go right in, he's expecting you." She gestured toward the door behind her. I thanked her and reached for the door handle. The door opened to display an office that was easily 50 feet by 50 feet. It was richly carpeted and furnished with beautiful antique furniture. There were several large oil paintings on the walls that depicted scenes from battles fought long ago. It felt like I was entering an art museum of historical military paintings.

The corner of the office had a curved wall that was floor-to-ceiling glass. There was a beautiful view of a small lake. Nurses and patients could be seen walking on a path around the lake. Some patients were on crutches and some were in wheel chairs, but they were all moving. Dr. Zeiss was seated behind a large walnut desk. He saw me looking at the strolling patients and said, "The best therapy is to have all patients exercise within hours of their surgery."

My mind was still on Monica and I couldn't resist asking where he had found her. He shrugged his shoulders and said that she was from Zurich. He hired his assistant from outside the country to insure that she had no contacts with the communist-controlled government of Poland. The best way to ensure this was to hire someone who was not from Poland. He had met her in Switzerland at a seminar and offered her a very handsome salary if she would work for him in Warsaw. He said that he paid her more for her salary then he officially earned as head of the hospital. She quickly learned the Polish language and cut her ties with her friends and family in Switzerland. Dr. Zeiss arranged for her to move to Warsaw and paid a large relocation allowance to compensate for her move. He said, "As beautiful as she is, I do not intend to risk losing the best employee I have ever had by having an affair with her." Dr. Zeiss said it was far better to enjoy her elegant beauty every day and keep their personal lives separate. He correctly sensed that I was aroused by Monica. With a twinkle in his eye and a large laugh he said, "You are just like all my male visitors. You are more interested in Monica than the work I am doing in my hospital." I laughed with him and decided that I would just have to get used to Monica while I was in Poland.

As I looked at the credenza behind his desk, I noticed a picture of Dr. Zeiss standing by a silver 1956 Mercedes-Benz gull wing coupe. My admiration of the car must have been as obvious to Dr. Zeiss as my fixation on Monica. He said, "Are you interested in collectible cars?" When I answered that I loved old cars, he said, "I collect cars and I will show you my collection later this evening."

There was a sculpture of a black raven on his desk and I asked him about it. He ignored my attempt to talk about the Black Raven Society and I took the hint that it was not the right time, but I was determined to talk with him about it later. Dr. Zeiss took off his white smock and slipped into a blue suit jacket with a small black raven pin on the lapel. As we walked out into the reception area of his office, Monica reminded him of his morning appointments and urged him to get a good night's sleep. She seemed genuinely concerned. What a lucky guy to have Monica looking out for his welfare.

We were headed for the elevator when I remembered the bag of gifts. I dashed back to his office and grabbed it. On an impulse, I gave Monica a bottle of Jim Beam and a roll of Kennedy half-dollars. It turned out to be one of the best impulses I have ever had. She became a friend and confidant because of that simple gift. In 1967, life in Poland was harsh and cruel and small kindnesses were rare. She accepted the gifts graciously and seemed so surprised at receiving them that I shook her hand with both of mine and assured her that it was my pleasure. She blushed, and looked even more beautiful in her embarrassment than she had when I first saw her. I turned and started toward the door just as Dr. Zeiss motioned for me to hurry; The elevator had just arrived.

CHAPTER SIXTEEN

POLISH HOSPITALITY

We got in the elevator and descended to the basement. It was the same floor where the Zim was parked. We passed the big sedan and walked over to an enclosed partition with a doublewide roll-up door. Dr. Zeiss pressed a clicker in the palm of his hand and the door automatically rolled up into the ceiling. Inside was a black 1958 BMW 507 roadster and a white 1967 250 SL Mercedes Benz roadster. The BMW was his and the Mercedes was Monica's. Dr. Zeiss gave it to her to celebrate her fifth anniversary as his private secretary.

I had known about the BMW 507 for several years. I studied all the published reports on it in Road & Track magazine. I had never seen one before. My jaw must have dropped 6 inches because Dr. Zeiss asked if I knew what kind of sports car it was. I replied, "BMW only made the car in 1957 and 1958. The total 507s made for both years was 253 and it's considered one of the best BMWs' ever made. The top speed is 137 mph and it does 0-60 in just under 7 seconds. It has an aluminum body on a tubular steel frame powered by a 507 c.c. V-8 engine with an aluminum block and heads. The entire car weighs less than

3000 lb." Dr. Zeiss looked at me with obvious surprise and said, "You know more about my car than I do; Lets go for a ride."

We roared out of the garage, and in less than a few seconds, we were traveling through Warsaw at speeds in excess of 70 mph. Dr. Zeiss knew the route well and made the high-speed drive seem very routine. It was a sunny afternoon and the top was down. The sports car engine had a deep race-car sound. People on the street turned and watched as we sped by. Most of Warsaw has traffic circles rather than intersections and lights, and a skillful driver can go through the traffic circles without slowing down. Dr. Zeiss was more than a skillful driver: He was like a grand prix driver with a death wish. We actually accelerated as we got closer to the center of Warsaw. At one point a motorcycle policeman pulled out and gave chase. At 85 MPH he pulled close enough to see that it was Dr. Zeiss and he waved a salute and turned around. As we raced off into a crisp spring evening, I realized that I was riding with the closest thing to a living-god that existed in Warsaw in 1967. Dr. Zeiss could do whatever he wanted and millions of adoring Polish citizens would stand by and let him do it. It was exciting to be with him, and even though he drove recklessly, I felt safe. I felt that we would become fast-friends and confidants.

We traveled along the northwest quadrant of Warsaw until the city faded into a rural countryside. After about 30 minutes we arrived at his home. It appeared to be about a 25 acre farm. We entered through a guarded gate and drove up to a large home that had barns, stables and a huge six-car garage. It could have been a farm in Kentucky. It was easily the most beautiful estate for miles in any direction. Dr. Zeiss used an automatic opener and the garage door raised to reveal a Mercedes 300 SL gull wing coupe and a 1964 Ferrari Lusso coupe. There was also a Zim just like the one I rode in earlier, but it was out of character with the other trophy cars in the garage. The garage also had its own gas pump and a full mechanic's workshop. I didn't know how he was able to choose what to drive to work.

We left the garage and walked through an arbor to the main house. We went inside and were greeted by a warm fire in the main entry room. I met Dr. Zeiss' wife, Katherine who was busy in the kitchen preparing dinner. I opened my briefcase and gave Dr. Zeiss the remaining bottle of Jim Beam, a bottle of Crown Royal, and a carton of cigarettes. I also gave him two rolls of Kennedy half-dollars. He thanked me for the gifts and put the whisky, and cigarettes in his liquor cabinet. The Kennedy half-dollars were placed in a drawer in a nearby desk. It had been a few years since Kennedy's death, but he was still very popular in Eastern Europe. Dr. Zeiss particularly liked the Kennedy half-dollars and he remarked that Kennedy was a hero to all the patriots in Europe. He was little known and admired from afar until his speech in Berlin. After that everyone fell in love with the man and his goals for world peace. He indicated that he intended to save the Kennedy coins and share them with his special friends.

He got a bottle of Belvedere vodka out of his liquor cabinet and asked if I had ever tried it before. He remarked, "It is made in Poland and is considered to be the best Vodka in the world." I told him I had tried it and thought it was very good. He poured two 4-oz. glasses of this white lightning and gave me one. We sat down and we started to talk. He wanted to know all about Stanislaw and I told him as much as I knew. He said, " You've got your work cut out for you. Two World Wars have been fought near Pionki and there was at least one tank battle fought there." He said he hadn't been there since before the last world war, but when he was there in the late 1930s, it was a beautiful area of small farms. World War I had passed over the area without any battles being fought in the town. He also mentioned that the area was close to Russia and the inhabitants were a mix of Russian and Polish ancestry.

Dr. Zeiss added, "I doubt Stanislaw has any surviving family. Winters in that area are cold, and a lot of Polish citizens perished in the harsh winters of the last few years. I asked about an interpreter and he reminded me of his brother who would be glad to help. Dr. Zeiss repeated the comments made to me at the lawn party in Seattle the previous summer. His brother worked for the Polish government in the intelligence department and his assigned task was to look for missing persons. He was one of two-dozen Polish government officials who would be qualified to find my deceased client's heirs. I confided in Dr. Zeiss my fear that someone in the Polish government might manufacture heirs to steal the money. He said, "It's not possible. It would be too easy to find out when they tried to spend the money." He also pointed out that if I found the heirs myself, there would be no doubt as to their authenticity: Nobody could manufacture a lifestyle and family tree that would match up with what I already knew about Stanislaw. I agreed, and explained that I wanted some safeguards to ensure that my report to the court was complete and accurate. He smiled grimly and said, "Nobody could fake the Polish peasant lifestyle." He reminded me that I was the only one that knew the names of any of Stanislaw's relatives and manufacturing heirs without knowing what to name them would be impossible.

I asked Dr. Zeiss when I could meet his brother. He replied by inviting me to spend the night and said he would send a car for his brother first thing in the morning. I tried to get him to talk about the Black Raven Society but he refused. He said that the pin used to be worn only by survivors of the Polish underground army for recognition, but in recent times many Poles who were old enough to fight had adopted the pin as their "badge of honor." He said "It doesn't have the meaning it used to." I told him the story I heard from Clarence the previous evening and he admitted that most of it was true. He looked at me with tears in his eyes and said, "I am trying to forget about all of my friends that I lost in the battle to save Warsaw. I hope you will not be offended if we do not discuss the war any further."

I said, "Let's talk cars." And we did. I told him about all the cars I had since my first 1952 Chevrolet convertible in high school to the 1965 Ford Mustang GT convertible that I was driving now. He showed me pictures of several cars that he had bought since the war. I asked him, "Where is the best place to buy classic European cars?" He gave me the name of a car dealer in Germany, Harold Daimler. Harold was a second-generation German car dealer in Stuttgart and a distant relative of the Daimler that founded the Mercedes-Benz company. That is where Dr. Zeiss bought his cars. He highly recommended Harold as a reliable classic car dealer. I wrote down the name and phone number and decided to pay Mr. Daimler a visit, if I could arrange my trip home to include a stop in Stuttgart.

We heard a small bell telling us that dinner was ready. Katherine was a pleasant middle aged housewife that seemed devoted to her husband. She stayed in the background and let him enjoy the limelight. The dinner was excellent. Katherine could have gotten the head chef's job at the Bristol Hotel. She started with a chilled soup with shrimp and followed up with a main course of wild turkey that Dr. Zeiss had shot the previous weekend. She had flavored the turkey with rice stuffing laced with almonds and raisins. She covered each serving of turkey and rice with a thick orange brandy sauce that blended all the flavors together. There were fresh chanterelle mushrooms that she had picked that morning from the north part of their farm.

For dessert she had baked a Muslin Baba that is best described as a Polish cake that is a cross between a crepe and a soufflé. It was dusted with powdered sugar and accompanied by a small glass of vintage sherry in beautiful crystal snifters.

After dinner Dr. Zeiss and I retired to the sitting room and talked about cars, our mutual doctor friends in Seattle and life in general. I asked about the opera and how hard it was to get tickets. He replied not hard at all. The performances were always sold out because the ticket scalpers could double their money reselling the tickets: It was the only performing art in town.

Dr. Zeiss was a patron of the Warsaw Opera and had a box. He said if I was available Sunday night he would be glad to take me to dinner in Warsaw and to the opera afterward. I gratefully accepted subject to my being available. It was getting late and we were both tired. I said good night to Katherine who was still in the kitchen and Dr. Zeiss showed me to a small guest room. He brought me a nightshirt and said to leave my underclothes and shirt by the door and his maid would wash them and have them ready in the morning. This was as good as the service at the Bristol Hotel. I washed up and slipped into the nightshirt and slid under the feather bed comforter. I could hear the farm animals and occasionally a dog barking. It was a very peaceful night and I slept soundly.

507 BMW

Mercedes Benz 300 SL Gull-Wing

Two favorite cars of Dr. Zeiss

CHAPTER SEVENTEEN

VALDIMER

The next morning I heard a rooster crow and lazily climbed out of bed. My room had a complete Western-style bathroom and I quickly showered and shaved. When I came out of the bathroom, my shirt and underclothes from the previous night were on the bed, washed and ironed to perfection. I got dressed and started downstairs. Sounds were coming from the sitting room. As I approached, a saw that Dr. Zeiss was conversing in Polish with a short, stout man in a black suit, holding a black hat in his hand. He looked like one of the "Blues Brothers" only bald. Dr.Zeiss saw me and walked over to greet me. With his arm around my shoulder he said, "Graham, come and meet my brother Valdimer." The man in the black suit stood up, bowed stiffly, and said in English, "It is my pleasure to meet you, Mr. Taylor." I encouraged him to call me Graham. Dr. Zeiss motioned for us to come into the dining room. Katherine prepared a light breakfast of hard boiled fresh farm eggs and fresh baked bread. There was also Western style coffee. I complimented my host on a fine cup of coffee, the best I had received in Poland. Valdimer remarked that he didn't like it as much as the traditional

Polish espresso. Apparently, Dr. Zeiss had developed a taste for Western coffee on his many trips to the United States and he always served it at his home.

I started telling Valdimer about Stanislaws' heirs. Valdimer stressed that he was on a social visit to his brother's home and said, "Anything I say is not an official act of the Polish government." He seemed very uncomfortable and not as sure of my sincerity as his brother was. I retrieved my briefcase and showed Valdimer the old Polish letters and some of my court documents. He wanted to see some identification and over the protests of Dr. Zeiss, I obliged. It was obvious that these two brothers were light years apart in just about everything they did. Gradually Valdimer began to trust me and became more involved in the heir search conversation. He got out a detailed map of Southern Poland and we located the town of Pionki. Valdimer indicated that this town was on the southern edge of the Kosienise region and that it was very remote. The area was mountainous and had some of the last virgin pine forests in Poland. The land was too rugged to log, and the peasants that lived there were among the poorest in Poland. Their homes were clustered in groups of 30 to 100 mud huts depending on how many people the farmland around these hamlets could support. He said they basically lived in an area that nobody wanted, as it had no useful purpose. The Catholic Church was the supreme force in their lives and supplied a church school system and social life to the faithful. He said that it was so non-strategic that the two World Wars could have passed over the Lanski hamlet and left it untouched. Suddenly he asked to see my file again and I watched as he turned to the sixth letter written by Aneskia. He explained that a town the size of Pionki could have several Catholic churches and a good starting place would be to look for a Catholic priest named Father Roland who presided over a Catholic church in Pionki in 1916. He used the phone and called his office. After a few minutes he put his hand over the phone and asked how many U.S. dollars I brought with me and how much could I give him for expenses. I reached in my briefcase and pulled out a banded stack of 100 one-dollar bills and tossed it in his lap and said, "Here's your retainer." He said a few words into the phone and hung up. As he started counting the money, I saw beads of perspiration forming on his forehead. Dr. Zeiss began to snicker and Valdimer shot him a dirty look. I said that I would give Valdimer $100 in small bills each day that he helped me but that if we didn't find anyone by the weekend, I was going home. He told me he had just told his office that he was sick and then said, "I am at your disposal for the next three days." I asked whether he had any luck with his inquiry about Father Roland and he replied that he had second thoughts about leaving any clues for his office to use to figure what we were up to. Any information about Father Roland could be found in Pionki. I asked him how soon could we could leave and he said, "If we hurry, we can be in Pionki by lunch time."

Valdimer spoke English with a strong Polish accent

and was sometimes hard to understand. But, he was alert and responsive to everything I said and if I listened carefully I could communicate with him with modest difficulty. He knew several Polish dialects and I decided that I would take a gamble on him and hire him as my guide and interpreter. I crossed my fingers, hoping he could be trusted. I couldn't have found another driver or interpreter without someone like Dr. Zeiss helping me and since he vouched for Valdimer, I figured that this was about the best I could hope for.

Valdimer and I got ready to leave, and we said good by to Katherine. Dr Zeiss was ready to leave for his hospital rounds and walked with us out to the garage area. I had already collected the things I had brought with me. Apparently Valdimer had packed in anticipation of a two-or three-day trip, as he had a small suitcase in the rear of his car. Dr. Zeiss opened the garage door closest to the house and showed me his prize Lusso Ferrari. He got in and it started with the first twist of the key. We watched as he slowly backed it out of the garage. Apparently the spring sunshine told him it was a "Ferrari" kind of day.

I saw a look of absolute envy on Valdimer's face and realized that the good Doctor was engaging in the old family game of "sibling rivalry." He was rubbing Valdimer's nose in the fact that he had accumulated more worldly possessions than Valdimer had. With a roar and a screech of tires Dr. Zeiss raced down the driveway leaving us in a cloud of dust. Valdimer muttered under his breath

That his brother was going to kill himself in one of those stupid Italian cars that he insisted upon driving.

Valdimer's car was constructed mainly of plastic. It was a 1961 Messerschmitt two-door, three-wheel vehicle that was powered by a one cylinder two-stroke engine. It ran on a mixture of gas and oil and had a top speed of about 50 mph. He was very proud of it and mentioned that he was the only person in his building who owned a car. Dr. Zeiss had seen the Messerschmitt when he bought his 300 SL in Stuttgart and brought the funny little car home on the same truck as his 300 SL. He gave it to Valdimer as a present for his 40th birthday. Ordinary Polish citizens could not import cars but Dr. Zeiss could do whatever he pleased. When I tried to open the door, the handle broke off in my hand. I thought Valdimer was going to cry. I reached in my wallet and pulled out a $20 bill and asked if this was enough to fix it. His eyes bugged out like Marty Feldman's and in a flash the tears turned to a big smile and he slapped my hand and said, "You sure know how to solve problems." From that point on we were fast friends. Whenever he was upset, a few U.S. Dollars would make him the happiest man in Poland. He inserted the handle in the door, gave it a twist, and suddenly it was working again. I sensed that I was the victim of the old, "Broken door handle swindle." As we loaded up and started back toward Warsaw, I decided that my new employee was going to earn that extra $20. After a few miles, the highway came to a major intersection and we turned south at a large road arrow with the name KRAKOW on it.

We traveled south going through alternating bands of tall pine trees and lush farmland. Farmers were conducting the first mowing of their hay. All the work was being done by hand with huge scythes just like the ones in the "Grim Reaper" cartoons. The peasants swung their scythes in unison like a synchronized ballet. They were in a long row and appeared to be staggered according to their height. They moved in a straight line but the stronger and taller workers were in the front and the line trailed back from the lead point. Valdimer said, "The man on the point is the leader. By having the workers aligned by order of their strength and height, he can keep an eye on every worker." It was a beautiful sight. Valdimer asked if I wanted to know how they kept swinging their scythes in such precise rhythm. When I said, "Yes," he pulled over at a place where the workers were nearing the road. He stopped and motioned to get out of the car. As soon as I opened the door, I heard voices singing a melodic folk song. The swings of their scythes were timed to the beat of the song they were singing. The beautiful colors, the warm sun and the fresh grass being raked into piles by the children, reminded me of some of the Van Gogh paintings I had studied in college. The spring hay was being spread out to dry; In the distance we saw other Peasants raking up hay from previous cuttings and piling it into pyramid-shaped haystacks. Everything was being done by hand. A similar scene had likely been performed here for over a thousand years. The blue sky, the yellow haystacks and the colorful peasants impressed upon me how beautiful rural Poland was, an observation repeated many times during my stay.

We continued on until we came to the town of Radom. Valdimer drove towards the center of the city and joined a two-block long line of trucks and cars waiting at what appeared to be the only gas station in town. While we waited vendors came by the car and for a few coins provided by Valdimer we relaxed and enjoyed Polish sausage in freshly made buns and some good local Polish beer.

After what seemed like an hour it was our turn at the pump. Valdimer showed the attendant a small card that allowed him to purchase the rationed petroleum products. The octane of the gas was about 75 and I doubt if U.S. cars could have run on it. Valdimer filled up the Messershmitt's four-gallon tank and also filled a couple of two-liter cans he had fastened inside the engine compartment. He bought some oil and mixed it with the fuel. I suddenly realized that with a rear engine car and two cans of gas strapped to the inside of the engine compartment, the Messerschmitt was a traveling bomb.

Valdimer paid for the fuel. I was surprised to see that it was 100 zlotys per gallon. That was about $6 a gallon at the official exchange rate. No wonder only the rich had cars. Valdimer smiled and said with pride that he could go 90 miles on a gallon of gas. Maybe the Messerchmitt wasn't so bad after all. It was so ugly that it developed an ugly duckling kind of charm and got better looking with every mile. I was actually enjoying riding in it.

We headed back toward the highway we had come from, but just before we got to it we took a sharp right turn on to a black top road that had a road sign that said Pionki. The road wasn't very smooth and we had to cut our speed to about 25 MPH. I'm not sure if it was a back road or the only way to get to Pionki, but at least we were headed in the right direction. We had driven about three hours, passing a few small villages along the way. We rounded a bend, and in a valley about a mile to the southeast we saw smoke coming from hundreds of chimneys. This had to be Pionki. The road became worse and suddenly we were on a one lane paved road that was full of pot holes.

When we got to the outskirts of the little town, we saw a sign that said Pionki. We started looking for the town's Catholic church. There were three church steeples to choose from and as we drove from steeple to steeple, we realized they were all Catholic churches. We decided to start our inquiry at the largest one. We found a small parking area near the plaza in front of the largest church and parked the Messerschmitt between a horse-drawn hay wagon and a manual pushcart. We crossed the plaza and entered the church through a side door. We waited in a pew at the back until a priest appeared. He looked about 75 and walked somewhat bent over. He had come out to freshen up the candle alter. We walked up to him and Valdimer pulled out his credentials identifying him as a Polish government official. He spoke in Polish asking the Priest whether he had ever heard of a Father Roland. The Priest was surprised and somewhat startled by the abrupt approach of Valdimer. I spoke and asked the Priest whether he spoke English. He said in perfect English, "Of course my son. Most of the Priests in Poland are trained to speak many languages." I explained that I was from Seattle, Washington, and that Valdimer was my guide. The priest said that Father Roland was a local priest before the Second World War but he died in the late 1930s. His church was at the North edge of town and his replacement came from my part of the United States. Father Patrick was the junior priest in town and the priest said we could find him at the small church in St. Mary's Square, which was the same one that Father Roland served at until his death.

I put several U.S. Dollars in the collection box by the door and we went back to the Messerschmitt. We got directions to the church in St. Mary's Square and were relieved to find it was only a short distance away. As we wound our way through the town, we saw many Polish residents on foot. We saw a few motorcycles but the rest of the vehicles we saw in Pionki were horse-drawn or oxen-drawn wagons. The town commercial center included a small hardware shop, several bars, a bakery, a grocery store and a couple of curbside vegetable stands.

We didn't see any stores that had consumer goods or clothes for sale. Everyone we passed stared at us as if we were from a distant planet. One man stumbled and fell as we drove by. He turned his head to follow us and didn't watch where he was walking. I could sense that Valdimer was nervous and worried that we were too high of a profile for this rural region.

I assured him that everything we were doing was legal and if we followed our plan and kept looking for Stanislaw's relatives, we would not get into any trouble. He seemed more relaxed then and a few minutes later we pulled into St. Mary's Square.

CHAPTER EIGHTEEN

FATHER PATRICK

I asked Valdimer to stay in the car as I suspected that the church and Polish government, (which he represented), did not get along very well. It was a prudent move. The church was on the northern edge of the square. I went up the stairs alone, and tried the door. It was locked. There was a big round ring that served as a doorknocker and I beat it a couple of times. After a few moments I hit it again. After what seemed like five minutes a voice on the other side of the door said something in Polish. I asked in a loud voice, "Do you speak English? I am looking for Father Patrick." In a few moments a small six-inch square door opened and a voice said, "Who is looking for Father Patrick?"

I said, "I am Graham Taylor a lawyer from Seattle, Washington and I have come a long way to locate some missing relatives of one of my deceased clients." I stuck my business card through the small hole and in a minute the door opened. A red-faced, jolly Irish-Catholic priest grabbed me and said, "Come in out of the cold, laddie." He was very excited to see someone from Seattle and in a rush began asking questions about Seattle and the Puget Sound area. He had a bottle of wine on a table behind him and a half filled glass beside it. He said, "Let's have a glass of wine and talk." He poured me a large glass of red wine and we started a lengthy conversation.

Father Patrick attended Seattle University, a prominent Catholic college in downtown Seattle during World War II. He was born in Shannon, Ireland and entered divinity school to escape from his bleak homeland. After becoming a priest, he went to Seattle in the hope of becoming a missionary in the Seattle University Asian Development Program. He started in 1940, but the allies were soon at war with Japan and most of Asia became a war zone. All of Seattle University's Asian programs were shut down. He indicated that the war brought all the conscientious objectors out of the woodwork, and soon the Catholic system had more priests than places to put them. He said that he had been in trouble with his superiors in Seattle for an alcohol problem. They didn't know what to do with him and kept a close eye on his activity. After the war they decided that he was not suitable to resume their Asian Development Program because of his drinking problem. Father Patrick's mother was Polish, and he spoke Polish fluently. That, combined with the Catholic need to rebuild the Catholic religion behind the Iron Curtain, resulted in his being sent to Pionki to re-open this old parish. I told him I was the attorney for Swedish Hospital, which is located right across the street from Seattle University. He said he was very familiar with my hospital, having visited the de-tox unit several times. I commented, "The Jesuit Priests that run Seattle University are certainly no strangers to alcohol." He nodded vigorously and then, with a shrug said, "I am disappointed that my career will end in this small church in southern Poland simply because, on more than one occasion when I had been drinking, I said things to my superiors that insulted them. I was given the choice of leaving the priesthood or taking this assignment." Then he said with a twinkle in his eye, "The best kept secret about this old church is the basement wine cellar I found behind a brick wall when I re-opened the church in 1950."

Apparently Father Patrick had developed quite a large Sunday crowd because he served excellent, well-aged wine for communion. The wine cellar was down several flights of steep, rickety stairs and he was able to make the trip only once a week. Unfortunately he usually started drinking the wine as soon as he got it upstairs. He said with a grin, "Got to be sure it's safe for my flock." Then with a frown he added, "On more than one occasion there wasn't much wine left for those taking communion." He had never told his Catholic peers about his hidden wine cellar and had no plans to do so. He trusted me to keep his secret and laughed when he said, "My superiors deserve to have me help them dispose of all this old wine. What do they expect, putting an Irish lush in charge of a large wine cellar with a church on top of it."

In 1950 he was assigned to this small parish and was

asked to re-open this 500-year old church. At the time it had been closed for over 10 years. When Father Roland passed away the congregation he developed in the Kozienice district to the north, faded back into the harsh land they had come from. Father Patrick explained that the small villages to the north were higher in elevation and had no electricity or running water. The villagers had no phones, and were too poor to have radios. For all practical purposes, they were totally cut off from the rest of the world. He likened their plight to that of the clans in the Appalachian and Ozark Mountains in the United States. He said that Father Roland was legendary for his treks into the wastelands of the region and for the lost souls he collected and brought back to this church. He surmised that my missing clients were among those villagers somewhere to the north. By now our glasses were empty. Father Patrick lifted the wine bottle and saw that it too was empty.

Then he exclaimed, "Enough of this Polish talk. Tell me about Seattle." He struck a match and lit an old kerosene lamp and beckoned me to follow him. He led us to a small doorway that turned into a darkened stairway with a small gate at the top. He motioned to me to keep my empty wine glass with me. Using an old key, he opened the gate and with the lamp in one hand, his empty wine glass under his arm and his other hand on the stair rail, he started down a very steep old spiral stairwell. He asked again to hear about Seattle. I answered by recounting the same story I told the Clemshaws a few nights earlier. When I mentioned the Seattle World's Fair, he stopped and asked several questions about it. I promised to send him some souvenirs from the fair, and he was elated at the prospect. He said he had tried to get permission to return and see the fair, but the church wouldn't pay his travel expenses and he had no money of his own. In this lonely outpost, he had been unable to get any information about the fair. The buildings for the fair were being constructed about the time he left Seattle. All he ever saw were holes in the ground near the Seattle Center. He particularly wanted a photograph of the Space Needle. To his delight, I opened my briefcase and gave him one. Before I left Seattle I had purchased several postcards showing the Space Needle, thinking that someone would ask about it. I was able to steer the conversation back to my heir search and got him to focus on whether there were any church records that could locate my deceased client's heirs.

He said, "Come with me and we'll have a look at the old records." We resumed our walk down the flight of stairs. He stopped at the first landing in front of a large cabinet and said, "Your visit calls for a celebration." He opened the cabinet and pulled out a large bottle of wine. He uncorked it and poured each of us a full glass of wine. He then grabbed the bottle, the lantern and his full glass of wine and headed down the stairs. He winked at me and said, "Would you like to see my hidden wine cellar? I'll show it to you if you keep it's location secret."

I had to smile: Here I was, stumbling down a pitch

black, steep flight of stairs in a 500-year old church in a remote corner of Communist Poland with a glass of wine in one hand and my briefcase in the other. I was being led by an alcoholic Irish priest who didn't know what we were looking for. He seemed more intent on showing me his treasured wine cellar than helping me locate my missing heirs. I hoped for the best and forged ahead. At the bottom of the second flight of stairs was a brick wall with a large bookcase in front of it. The bookcase was on hidden rollers and Father Patrick slid it sideways with one hand. Behind the bookcase was a hidden room that was easily 50 feet by 50 feet. It was full of rack after rack of musty wine bottles covered with cobwebs. We proceeded through the dark room, lit only by the lantern Father Patrick was holding. At the rear of the room was another staircase, narrower and steeper than the last.

At the bottom of the third flight of stairs Father Patrick turned to me and said, "Take a good swig of wine, Graham, you're going to need it." He took a long drink of wine from his glass, and I did the same from mine. He refilled our glasses from the magnum that was under his arm. He tucked the bottle back in his robe, straightened his shoulders, and led me down a passageway. Suddenly the path widened, opening out into an underground cave about 20 feet across. The yellow glow from the lantern threw strange shadows on the walls and for a second I thought I saw bones and skulls embedded in the walls. As my eyes adjusted to the light, I realized to my horror, that

I was right. Bones and skulls had been made into ornamental mosaics covering all four walls of the room. There were two altars on opposite sides of the room that had pyramids of skulls on them. There were old empty candleholders on each side of the altars that suggested that services of some kind were held in this room a long time ago. Large leg bones formed fans over the altars and rib bones had been laced into latticework on the ceiling. Finger and toe bones had been formed into balls that looked like a morbid thistle from hell. I was in both shock and awe, as I never expected a medieval, satanic looking sanctuary in the bowels of this old church.

Father Patrick was chuckling at my obvious panic. I must have been shaking like a leaf. He said, "Take another swig, Graham, and get a hold of yourself. They can't hurt you. They have been dead for hundreds of years." He then reminded me that this church dated back to the fifteenth century when all priests were considered saints. When priests died, they saved their bones and fashioned them into these religious shrines. Sometimes they made alters with them. Other times they used the bones for intricate wall or ceiling designs. He said the practice was not unusual for the fifteenth century, but most churches had removed the old bone sanctuaries as too gruesome for modern-day parishioners. This collection of bones was hidden, three floors down in the sub-basement of the old church. The leaders of the Polish Catholic church that sealed off the wine cellar and bone chapel had been dead for decades. It was doubtful whether anyone other than Father Patrick and those he confided in knew of it's existence. I hope that if it is discovered that it is kept as a historical site. It was an unusual way to honor the departed priests. The more time I spent in the room, the more I appreciated the artistic way the bones were displayed.

Father Patrick stumbled a bit and moved towards an altar to his right. He mumbled, "I think the records are over here." Each altar had shelves and drawers behind it. After a minute or so he said, "This isn't the right place." He moved over to an altar on the far wall, fumbled through some drawers and announced, "Here they are." He emerged from behind the alter with an old weathered cardboard file folder. There were numerous documents and ledgers sticking out of it. It looked very disorganized. There was a round table in the middle of the room. A hook hung down from the bones on the ceiling. Father Patrick hung the lamp on the hook and began spreading out the papers he took from the file folder. He announced, "Here are Father Roland's records." He thumbed through the files and found the entries made just before Father Roland died. The last record of donations made to his parish was in the month before his death, May 12, 1938. Father Patrick asked, "Do you recognize any names?" I scanned the list and in the middle of the second page was the name "Aneskia Wierzynek," followed by the words: 1 Zloty, Vil Lanski 2. Father Patrick saw my finger pause at Aneskia's name and asked, "Do you recognize a name?" I responded that the first name was correct, but I had never seen the last name before. He said, "That may be her married name." I nodded in agreement. Father Patrick said that "Vil" was short for "village," and the "2" was the number of the hut in the village. This had to be Stanislaw's sister and she must have been alive in the spring of 1938, when Father Roland made the entry in the ledger. Father Patrick agreed. The parish was so small that this Aneskia was probably the Aneskia I was looking for.

He suggested that, since there had been an exchange of letters, someone at the Pionki Post Office might know if the village of Lanski still existed. It was possible that Lanski residents on occasion still came to the Pionki post office to post letters or collect mail. We went back upstairs. It was obvious that Father Patrick was feeling the effects of all the wine he had consumed. He negotiated the stairs fairly well, but tripped on the top step of the last flight and nearly fell. I grabbed his arm and steadied him as we walked towards the front door. He put down the wine and admitted that in his happiness to see someone from Seattle he had imbibed a little too much "fruit of the vine." He was a kind old gentleman and I tried not to be judgmental about his drinking problem. I promised myself that I would try to see him again. We were on the ground floor of the church and suddenly it struck me how dim the light was. The windows were so covered with dirt that hardly any light got through. There was no electricity and only the lamp carried by Father Patrick gave off any light. The church had pews that would seat about thirty people. This was definitely the last outpost for a priest's assignment.

When we reached the front door of the church, I opened it, and we walked out into the warm spring sunshine. The light was blinding after being in the dark church. Father Patrick pointed to a gray building a block south and said, "There's the post office." He gave me a hug and I gave him a $20.00 bill for his poor box. He thanked me and asked me to stop on my way back to Warsaw and tell him what I found. I said I would if we had time. I said goodbye and headed for the Messerschmitt where I found Valdimer sound asleep. I woke him up and told him of my visit with Father Patrick and directed him to the gray building to the south. When he learned that it was the regional post office he panicked.

He was against going to the post office because he feared the low-level government officials there would ask too many questions. I insisted, and a few minutes later he was walking up the post office steps. He refused to park in front, preferring to keep his car out of view on a side street. This time we thought it better for me to stay in the car. He was back in less than ten minutes. He jumped in the car and said. "Lets get out of here." He backed up the street we had come down and just as we swung around the corner I saw a uniformed man come from the direction of the post office and look in our direction. He only got a fleeting glimpse of us as we turned the corner and sped out of sight. I asked, "What happened?" He said, "It looked easy at first. I went to the counter and asked for directions to a small village to the north called Lanski. The clerk at the counter asked an older postal employee working at the rear of the post office, whether he had ever heard of a village called Lanski. The older worker replied that it was about five miles past the end of the road to the King's hunting mountain. Then the older worker said that he hadn't seen anyone from Lanski for months and asked why I wanted directions to Lanski." I made the mistake of lying and said, "I am looking for the sister of a friend." Suddenly a policeman came out of the back room and headed towards me. He demanding to know why I was in Pionki and who did I know that lived in Lanski? I panicked and ran out of the post office and he chased me."

Valdimer was perspiring and badly frightened. He was breathing heavily and I made him loosen his tie. I offered to drive and he immediately pulled over, got out, and changed places with me.

I drove back to Father Patrick's church. Valdimer was slouched down trying to hide. I got out, ran up to the church door and knocked on the front door. Father Patrick opened up the 6"x 6" window, saw it was me and opened the door. I stepped inside and hurriedly told him what had happened at the post office. He made a dismissive motion with his hand and told me not to worry. He knew the postal worker and the old cop and said, "They are just nosy. They open and read everybody's mail. The old policeman was probably just curious about why you wanted information about Lanski."

Father Patrick cautioned me to tell my driver that stupid blundering could cause the authorities to detain one or both of us until they understood what we were doing. He said, "For some Pionki officials, it could take weeks for them to understand anything."

When I asked about the King's Hunting Mountain road, Father Patrick said that it started a few miles out of town and actually went to a mountain where the King of Poland used to hunt. He said, "No one hunts there anymore, and there are lots of wild animals. Be careful of snakes. The village of Lanski must be on the same road somewhere on the other side of the King's historical hunting grounds." He warned me that there were rumors of bandits living in the hills around the King's Hunting Mountain, and there was no Polish police protection beyond the outskirts of Pionki. I joked that no police of any kind would be a great relief to my driver, Valdimer. Father Patrick told me to drive to the last street north of the square, take a left and then a right at the first bridge across the river. That road would turn into the King's Hunting Mountain Road about three miles from town. Again I bade farewell to Father Patrick and raced down the church steps.

I jumped into the Messerschmitt and we headed out of town on the route recommended by Father Patrick. I drove and Valdimer remained slouched far down in his seat. I told him what Father Patrick said, but he wasn't reassured. He just wanted to get out of town as quickly as possible. This was another example showing how police terrified the people behind the Iron Curtain in the mid sixties. What a difference from the pot-smoking hippies of the United States who congregated in mass to challenge the government's authority during that same time period.

Just to provoke Valdimer a little, I stopped at a bakery and got some rolls, some local cheese, and a couple of chicken sandwiches. Valdimer said he wasn't hungry. I drove a few blocks and stopped by a small park to enjoy the food. We had beer, given to us by Dr. Zeiss, and I offered one to Valdimer. He took it, and after a couple of sips, he asked for a sandwich. I relaxed, and so did Valdimer as he realized that no one was chasing us.

Chapel of Bones

Messerschmitt Similar To Valdimer's

CHAPTER NINETEEN

THE ROAD TO LANSKI

After our picnic, I continued to drive Valdimer through the streets of Pionki. I enjoyed driving his funny little car and I even stopped and slid open its plastic sliding roof to let in the sunshine. We both felt a lot better after lunch.

After a few turns, we were on a road on the south side of a river that bordered the north edge of the town. We came to a bridge, took a sweeping right turn, and crossed the river that was the north boundary of Pionki. As soon as we crossed the bridge, my brave companion sat back up in his seat and decided that it would be all right if he started driving again. He muttered something about my not being insured.

We were passing a small outdoor market and I saw a stall selling men's clothes. I pulled over. I had planned to have my clothes washed at the hotel, but now that we were in the country, I was running out of essentials fast. Valdimer followed a few paces behind. I was able to buy a couple pair of underwear, a muslin peasant shirt and two pair of dark socks. Total cost: 13 Zloty.

As I returned to the car I gave Valdimer the keys and

got in the passenger seat. He went around to the driver's seat, got in and we headed north up the road. In a mile or two the pavement ended and the highway turned into a one-lane dirt road. We saw a small sign with an arrow that confirmed we were on the road to the King's old hunting grounds. The road was rough and we slowed to 20 mph. We had gone only a few hundred yards before we saw the first deer. Three bucks and a doe lazily watched us drive by as if cars were a regular sight. In another half-mile we spotted two black bears rolling and playing in the tall grass by the side of the road. When we drove by they stopped what they were doing and followed us for awhile. In the next few miles we saw hundreds of wild animals. There were more deer and small brown bears standing by the many rivers and streams we passed. At one crest in the road, a half dozen red fox ran across the road in front of us: a mother and her litter. They seemed interested in us, and stopped in the tall grass by the side of the road, to watch us pass. We were in a dense pine forest, and from the looks of the road we were the only ones that had used it for some time. Our wheels left small tracks on the dirt road and there were no other tracks to be seen. It hadn't rained since I came to Poland 5 days ago, so we were the only ones to use this road in at least five days.

The king's mountain was not much of a mountain. It was like one of our downtown hills in Seattle. It was no more than 1,500 feet high. What it lacked in height it made up for in charm. The beautiful pine forest and the abundant game confirmed that this rugged area was the game park of former Polish kings.

As we rounded a curve, Valdimer slammed on the breaks and screamed, "WILD BOAR." I'm not sure what he expected me to do, but I looked with interest at a brown hairy 75-pound pig with small tusks standing in the road ahead of us drinking out of a small puddle. It eyed our car and started pawing the dirt. It must have thought the Messerschmitt was some kind of streamlined animal. The boar was about the size of a big Springer Spaniel and did not look particularly menacing. I said, "For God's sake Valdimer, honk the horn and let's go." He honked several times but the pig wouldn't budge. I told Valdimer to drive forward and go around the pig. Valdimer drove a little closer and still the pig refused to move. I got out, intending to chase the pig away, but when I passed in front of the Messerschmitt, the boar charged. I thought it was bluffing and I yelled to scare it, but it kept coming.

When it was a few feet away and still charging full speed ahead, I realized it meant business. I dove up on the top of the car but the boar also jumped onto the Messer-schmitt and was still coming right at me. I rolled to the right as it turned its snout sideways and took a swipe at me. Luckily it missed. Its momentum carried it right over the car and as it slid by the sunroof, one of its tusks dug into the plastic and ripped a hole about 4 inches long before it tumbled over the car and landed on it's back in the middle of the road. It sat dazed, about 10 feet behind the car. It was obvious that its tusks were razor sharp. It was a mean little beast and I seized the opportunity to jump back into the car.

Valdimer put the car in gear and we took off, leaving the stunned wild boar behind us as quickly as possible. After we gained a few hundred yards on the nasty little porker we looked at each other and laughed. Valdimer thought I was a fool to face a wild boar and I agreed as I realized how close I had come to having one of my legs slashed open. We traveled another two and a half hours. I estimated that we had gone about 50 miles. We came to a clearing and saw what was left of several burned out buildings. Valdimer said that this must have been the old hunting lodge. It looked as though it had burned down 50 or more years ago. We stopped for a minute and then saw a continuation of the road on the other side of the clearing. We kept driving and in a mile or so the road turned into a grassy path with two ruts where vehicles had gone before us. The grass had almost grown over the path, but if you concentrated you could see the route. We went much slower as the little car was having trouble pushing down the three-foot tall grass in our path. As we crested a small hill, we startled a covey of quail that had made their nest in the tall grass between the two ruts in the road. The quail fluttered up with such a flurry that Valdimer drove off the road. I thought to myself, "We better not break down if the road is used so seldom that birds can nest in the middle of it."

The right front wheel got stuck on a mud ridge. We

both got out and lifted it up and pulled the little car back on the two ruts that served as a road. We continued for about five miles until the path turned into mud. We were soon hopelessly stuck. The mud was 18 inches deep and the car became high centered. The little car only weighed a few hundred pounds, but Valdimer was weak and I couldn't lift it by myself. Valdimer was worried that no one used the road any more and we would have to walk over 50 miles for help. I pointed out that Lanski couldn't be too far ahead and started getting my stuff ready for a long hike.

I took off my shoes, tied the laces together, and threw my shoes around my neck. I put my socks in my briefcase, grabbed the sack with my clothes from the Pionki outdoor market, and said, "Come on Valdimer, let's go to Lanski. It can't be much farther and we can get plenty of help there to get your car out of the mud." He walked around his car and looked like he was going to have a nervous breakdown. I walked back, opened my briefcase, and gave him another $20.00. This was the universal antidote for Valdimer's Messerschmitt laments. He immediately pocketed the money and followed me, but he kept his shoes on. He said he was afraid of snakes. We walked about three miles, trying to follow the old path overgrown with grass.

Finally we came to a point where the path parted and went in two directions. I chose the right path because it seemed a little more traveled but with night approaching we were concerned. The countryside was looking more and more like well-tended farms with acres of wheat blowing in the wind. We walked another mile, and as we crested a small hill, we heard the first sounds of life since Pionki.

There were a dozen children playing in the grass, none of them over six years of age. The hill sloped away to a small valley. In the middle of the valley, about two miles away, was a small village comprised of a couple dozen mud huts with thatched roofs. In the distance we could hear the sounds of the village inhabitants preparing for dinner. The scene was like a painting out of a museum.

When the children saw us, four older girls ran screaming down the path towards the village. Another half dozen pulled back into the tall grass, and two three-to four-year old boys stayed in the path and stared up at us as if Mickey Mouse and Donald Duck had come to visit them. I said hello to the first one and gave him a candy bar. In an instant all of the kids except the girls that had run away surrounded me and I gave them each a candy bar from the box of Baby Ruths that I had brought with me. They had never seen a candy bar before and the Baby Ruth bars I gave them were treated like precious treasure. I had just won the Lanski children's patron saint of the year award. One very shy but polite little boy came up and said some Polish words that Valdimer said was a sincere thank you. I put the little guy on my shoulders and we all walked down the hill towards the village I knew had to be Lanski.

The May weather had been warm, but as dusk approached the air became crisp and I felt a slight chill as we walked the last half-mile towards the village with these children. I knew in my heart that Stanislaw's relatives were just a few strides ahead. The children were cheering and making so much noise that I was sure the residents in the village ahead heard us coming. The valley was a golden yellow with the new hay as yet uncut, and as the wind blew across the grain, we saw some activity around the thatched roof huts in the distance. I quickened my pace and walked briskly towards Lanski. Valdimer was dragging behind; he was worried about whether he would get in trouble for bringing me this far. I reassured him that he had nothing to fear, and said, "We are probably the first outsiders to visit Lanski in months." We soon found out it had been several years since Lanski had seen any visitors from outside their hamlet.

As we got closer I was able to count 25-30 small mud huts with thatched roofs. They were small rounded huts about twenty feet in diameter. Each hut had a small wisp of smoke coming out of a hole in its coned thatched roof. The little girls who had run away from us had reached the edge of the village. They were causing quite a commotion. It was dinnertime, and even from this distance, the tantalizing smells of what was being prepared made me realize that we hadn't eaten anything since our Pionki picnic almost six hours ago.

The excited little girls had roused most of the village out of their huts and many villagers were coming toward us. Older women were standing in the doorways of several of the huts with cooking utensils in their hands, motioning their families to come back for dinner. Then the older women saw us and put down their pots and joined the throng coming towards us. They all seemed very happy and very excited to have visitors.

I thought that this was a perfect way for me to discover Lanski. If I had been a Hollywood screenwriter I could not have imagined a better way for the young American lawyer to enter Stanislaw's birthplace in his quest to find his client's long lost relatives.

CHAPTER TWENTY

LANSKI

The throng met us about 100 yards from the village and we all walked towards the hamlet together. I was busy playing Santa Claus with what remained of the 48 Baby Ruth candy bars that I had brought from Seattle. My new found little buddy was playing Santa's helper and passing the bars out to those who hadn't received one yet. He was being very fair with his candy bar distribution and I was glad for his help as we were being mobbed.

Valdimer was trying to talk with some of the men that approached us, but he was having trouble with the dialect. I dropped alongside of him and listened and I noticed a lot of head shaking. Valdimer volunteered that they were speaking some sort of imperial Russian language mixed with a classic southern Polish dialect. He understood only part of it. I told him in jest that he had just been demoted from interpreter to driver. He said in a whine that he had confirmed that the hamlet we were approaching was Lanski and gave me a depressed look that reminded me of my cocker spaniel puppy when I left her in Seattle. I saw that I had hurt his feelings and quickly told him that I was just joking and he was still my interpreter.

As we neared the first hut, I put down the little boy who had been riding on my shoulders. There were still a half a dozen Baby Ruth bars left and I gave them to him. He ran into the village with all the other children chasing after him. Nearly all the doors to the huts were open and more people were coming out to join the crowd. We were walking down the central path of the village and I noticed that the huts were numbered, but they seemed out of sequence. The smallest numbers were in the middle of the village by a small circular fountain.

As we came closer to the fountain, I caught sight of hut 1. Just to it's right was hut 2. That was the number of Aneskia's hut in the church records. The door on hut two was closed. I walked directly to hut two and knocked on a heavy planked door held together by black wrought iron hinges. I heard a noise inside and after a minute or two the door opened, and an old woman stood in the doorway. Her clothes were clean but very old and worn out. Her dress was gray muslin and had numerous holes through the fabric. She was not wearing shoes. Her feet were wrapped in rags and she was very thin. I exclaimed, "ANESKIA?" She looked puzzled and responded "YA."

A hush fell over the crowd when they heard Aneskia speak. I motioned for Valdimer to follow me, and we stepped inside hut two and closed the door. After all these months, I felt a huge sigh of relief escaping from my lungs. I grabbed Aneskia in a hug and wept tears of joy. I had Stanislaw's sister in my arms and I knew everything was going to work out all right.

I think my sudden closing of her door and my hug frightened her, as she drew back towards the center of her hut. She understood Valdimer's Polish better than the other villagers and he was able to converse with her quite easily. He gave me a thumbs-up sign after speaking to her for a few moments. Later we learned that Aneskia had attended Father Roland's church school in Pionki and had learned Polish grammar there. Because of the church schooling she spoke traditional Polish as well as the dialect used in Lanski. We were able to make ourselves understood to Aneskia and Valdimer got assurances from her that she could translate if we needed help conversing with the villagers. I was a little nervous that the translation going through so many people might lead to misunderstandings.

I had some pictures of Stanislaw with me and I showed them to Aneskia. She recognized Stanislaw and began crossing herself in the traditional Catholic manner. She went to a small chest by her bed and took out an old set of rosary beads. She started talking so fast that Valdimer began to lose the translation. He said she was shifting back to the same dialect that the other villagers had used when we first came into town.

Valdimer spoke very slowly to Aneskia. He identified himself and told her that he worked for the Polish Government. I could see that she was terrified. I pulled Valdimer aside and told him that the last thing this old woman wanted to hear was that a Polish official was here to question her about her family. I played "hardball" with Valdimer and told him I wouldn't pay him unless he worked through me and said nothing further to any of the villagers unless it was to interpret something I said to them or they said to me. He accepted my criticism and instruction reluctantly.

I took the lead in conversation with Aneskia and I told her I was a lawyer from Seattle, Washington, a city in the United States of America. I was the attorney for her deceased brother Stanislaw. She looked at me and said in Polish, "Stanislaw? He died in 1916." This and our further conversation was translated by Valdimer.

I responded, "No he didn't, he lived in Seattle, Washington until he died last year." She said "Why are you in Lanski?" I told her that Stanislaw had died last December in Seattle and that he had left money in United States–dollars that I had brought to Poland to give to her and any other living relatives of Stanislaw." She crossed herself again and began to cry.

CHAPTER TWENTY-ONE

ANESKI

Suddenly Aneskia exclaimed, "What day in December did Stanislaw die?" I looked at my file and said, "He died on Dec. 6, 1966." She looked as though she had been struck by lightening. She moved back a step or two and sat down in an old wicker chair. She said over and over again, "December 6, December 6, December 6." She would shake her head in disbelief and say, " December 6," again and again.

Then she said with tears in her eyes, "Please ask my niece, Riadia, to come in and join us." I asked Valdimer to go out in the village and find Aneskia's niece and bring her into the hut. He opened the door, and to the crowd that had congregated outside Aneskia's door, he announced in his best Polish, "Riadia, please come inside, your Aunt Aneskia wants you to be with us."

A middle-aged woman came from the back of the crowd and said in English, "I am Riadia, what does Aneskia want?" Valdimer beckoned her to enter. She came in and immediately went to Aneskia and gave her a hug. She was very attractive but not what you would expect a relative of Aneskia's to look like. She had darker skin than her aunt and was slightly crippled. She was limping on a bad left leg and walking with the assistance of a cane. She spoke in broken English. She recognized me as English or American and assumed that I would converse in English. Her English was good but occasionally it broke down, and when it did, we turned to Valdimer and we were able to communicate in Polish, without any misunderstanding. The following conversations were the result of both Valdimer and Riadia's translation assistance. I felt totally comfortable with the accuracy of the information we were receiving.

Aneskia was in shock, and she started babbling to Riadia, and they both began crying in each other's arms. It took several minutes for Valdimer and me to figure out what was going on but finally we determined that it had to do with a vision Riadia shared with Aneskia in December of 1966.

Riadia was a Gypsy. She was found by Paul, Aneskia's brother lying by the Wista River, in the late spring of 1941. Paul had lost his 14-year old daughter to pneumonia the preceding winter. When he found Riadia, she shocked him by saying, "Paul, help me. My name is Riadia and I have hurt my leg." At hearing this young girl call him by name, Paul at first was frightened. He soon recovered and realized that this young woman needed his help. He carefully placed her on top of his wagon and brought her back to Lanski. Paul's family nursed Riadia back to health. She was almost the exact age of Paul's daughter and his other children immediately fell in love with her. With the blessing of the village, Paul's family soon adopted her. She has been a member of the Stocowski family ever since and is treated as blood family by all the relatives.

The entire village of Lanski soon learned of Riadia's unusual ability to forecast future events. From time to time, she would have visions of the future and also had the ability to gain an insight into the true motivation of people she touched. She never knew when these visions would come, but they were always preceded by a momentary trance. Riadia in her infrequent trances communicates with her deceased ancestors and with their help she accurately has visions of present or future events and proceedings. She has never been wrong in predicting future events when she emerges from one of her trances.

In November of 1966, Aneskia's feet were frostbitten and became infected. She thought about ending her life. All the family was concerned about her deep depression. They kept a close watch on her daily activities. Riadia told the family that Aneskia was suicidal and with everyone's blessing, she stayed with Aneskia until she got over her depression. She had many discussions with Aneskia, and once while talking about whether there was any hope for Aneskia's future. Riadia slipped into a trance. Upon emerging, she told Aneskia of a vision she had received while in the trance.

On this occasion, Riadia had a vision that she said came from a place far away and told her that Aneskia was going to be rich beyond her wildest dreams because of something that was happening at that very moment. Her trance ended before she learned what the event was but she was positive that the event would affect Aneskia and the rest of the Stocowski family's future forevermore. She was sure that it was an event of international significance. Shortly after hearing of Riadia's prediction, Aneskia's depression subsided and her attitude improved.

Aneskia got up from her chair and as she moved slowly towards the rear of her hut. She said, "If it had not been for Raidia's prophesy I would not be here today." Then with a long bony finger, she pointed to an old calendar on the wall. The date of December 6, 1966 had been circled. "This was the day of Riadia's prediction," she said, her eyes glowing, "It is the same day my brother died." She finished by saying "I have been waiting for someone or something to explain the significance of what happened on December 6, 1966. Please tell me about my long lost brother."

As soon as I recovered from the shock of Riadia's vision, I told Aneskia, for the next hour, of the long association my father and I had with Stanislaw. I told her what a good butcher he was and what a fine shop he built in Seattle. She asked why he had not written his family and told them of his good fortune. I thought for a moment that I should tell her about the letters that made Stanislaw abandon his family in Poland, but rationalized that bringing up the old lies would serve no useful purpose. It could ruin the rapport we were establishing with Aneskia, and could spread to the rest of the family. I told her that as long as I had known him, I had never seen him write anything and he probably didn't have any capability of communicating by letter. She nodded and mentioned that he refused to attend the Catholic school in Pionki, and used to tease her about her long trips into town. She accepted Stanislaw's illiteracy as the reason he didn't keep in touch with his family. I told her that I had been a friend with Stanislaw since I was six years old and that he had always given my family turkeys or beef roasts to enjoy on holidays. She asked whether he had ever married or had a family and I explained that he had been a bachelor all his life. I told her about Keiko and the way she had made him a part of her family. I also explained that Keiko was Stanislaw's personal representative and the person chosen by the Washington court to hold Stanislaw's belongings in trust until the heirs could be contacted and given the assets of his estate. I glorified his hotel room, as I didn't want them to think poorly of Stanislaw because of the small room he lived in. I told Aneskia what a fine businessman Stanislaw was, and how well the other merchants of the Seattle Public Market respected him. I went into detail about how good he was at saving his money and how he wanted it to go to his family in Poland. She leaned forward and motioned for me to repeat myself as if she didn't understand what I was saying. It was obvious that she was listening to every word I said and our conversation was making her very happy. Riadia seemed a little more skeptical and I reasoned that she might be able to perceive some of the fibs I was inserting in the conversation to make the situation more comfortable for everyone. She didn't say anything, but I saw her cock an eyebrow, when I said that Stanislaw had saved his money for his family in Poland.

Our conversation shifted to my questions about the Stocowski family tree. She told me that her parents were Ian and Inga Stocowski and they had five children, Peter, Marion, Stanislaw, Paul and Aneskia. Aneskia was the sole survivor of her siblings. Peter, who died in 1930, had two living sons, Peter Jr., who lived in Lanski, and Edward who lived in Warsaw. Marion died in 1939 with no children. Paul died in 1950, survived by three children: his adopted daughter Riadia, his daughter Jana and a son Merzec, all residing in Lanski. The family thought Stanislaw died fighting for the Americans in France in 1916.

Suddenly I realized that I had my inheritance profile, subject to formal proof. It looked like this:

IAN & INGA STOCOWSKI

•

•

•

PETER----------MARION----------STANISLAW----------PAUL-----------ANESKIA

Died 1930   *Died 1939*   *Died 1966*   *Died 1950*   *still alive*

•   •

•   •

PETER------EDWARD   JANA -------MERZEC-------RIADIA

I told Aneskia that according to the intestate laws of the state of Washington, the heirs listed in the profile of the family tree we had created would divide Stanislaw's estate into one-third shares. One third for each surviving brother or sister. This meant she would get one-third of the money that was in Stanislaw's estate. The children of her deceased brothers would share their deceased father's one-third share. This would include Riadia as the Washington probate laws included adopted children.

I calculated that there would be approximately $425,000.00 to split up after payment of all estate taxes and estate expenses: Aneskia's 1/3 share would be a little over $141,500.00, Peter and Edward would get a 1/6 share of about $70,750.00 and Jana, Merzec and Riadia's 1/9 share would be a little over $46,500.00.

I asked Aneskia and Riadia to call Peter, Jana and Merzec into the hut. Riadia went to the door and opened it. Standing on the doorstep, she called out their names. Three people stepped forward and Riadia ushered them into Aneskia's hut. With the help of Valdimer and Riadia we told them about Stanislaw's death. We also told each one that they were in the line of descent and what each stood to inherit. There was dead silence for a moment. Jana had to sit down and looked bewildered. The men gave each other long friendly hugs and with a smile on everyone's face, the hut turned into a place of celebration. Peter disappeared for a moment and came back with a small jug of Vodka.

Riadia explained that Peter was the village vodka distiller and that his vodka was very strong and very good. Aneskia got some small glasses and Peter filled them all and passed them around. We first drank a toast to Stanislaw. The vodka was strong, probably close to 120 proof. It was extremely smooth and could be sipped straight with no bite of any kind. I needed to clear up one item and that was the legality of Riadia's adoption. Technically, Riadia could not inherit her share unless there was proof of a legal adoption by Paul, but Jana and Merzec were the only ones who could challenge Riadia's right to her inheritance. I asked if they had any objection to her participation in the inheritance and they responded that they both thought of her as their sister. They volunteered that if she were cut out of the inheritance because of technicalities, they would share theirs equally with her anyway. I told them that I would prepare a waiver and release that would bind them to an acknowledgment that Riadia was their legally adopted sister. They both readily agreed to the proposal. I confirmed the family tree with Peter, Jana, Riadia and Merzec. I got the address of Edward in Warsaw, and planned to meet with him when we returned to the city.

We toasted the Stocowski family and I asked if they would like an advance of their inheritance. They all smiled and happily said yes. They were extremely happy at the prospect of getting some cash right away. I asked if they wanted Zlotys or U.S. dollars and in one voice they all said, "U.S. Dollars." I opened my briefcase and displayed the

$5,000 in cash I brought with me. When they saw the cash, their eyes got as big as baseballs. The $5,000 in cash was in small bills, which made it look like much more than it was. I decided to disburse $3,000 and gave Aneskia $1,000 cash, Riadia, Merzec and Jana $335 each and Paul $500. The men threw their bills in the air. And as they floated towards the floor, they scurried around grabbing as many bills as they could. They sat at Aneskia's kitchen table, and meticulously counted each bill until they each had the right amount. Then with a belly laugh they would throw them in the air again and start all over again. They did this several times. Everyone in the room was laughing with them. I used the Kennedy half-dollars as part of the payment and gave each of them several of the new coins. They all knew of this man who had spoken in Berlin, and they loved the coins. The coins were new and they carefully wrapped each coin in scraps of soft cloth that Aneskia provided. They treated the coins as jewelry, not something to spend.

It was getting dark, and we talked about where we were going to spend the night. Aneskia offered her home to Valdimer and me and said she would spend the night in Paul's hut. They invited us to stay for a day or two so that they could have a celebration in the village. We agreed and then Aneskia opened the front door of her hut and told the assembled villagers what had happened. They all cheered and joined in the celebration. The villagers greeted this kind of good news as if they had inherited the money. Aneskia remarked that everyone in the village was very close, and the throng was like an extended family. Good fortune for one was good fortune for all. There was never any sign of envy or jealously in any of my dealings with the inhabitants of Lanski.

Aneskia arranged for our dinner and everyone promised to meet at the community gathering spot near the fountain at about 8 that evening. Then Aneskia packed a few belongings and left with the others. In a few minutes Paul returned with two plates brimming with hot food and a fresh crock of vodka. Valdimer and I sat at the small table in Aneskia's hut and ate a very good stew, a dish that resembled a good Yankee pot roast. There were potatoes, carrots and very good meat, probably beef or lamb, all in a white cream sauce. We ate every bite and toasted each other with our success at finding Lanski and the Stowcowski heirs. After dinner, we laid down on the two feather beds in the hut and took a three-hour nap.

CHAPTER TWENTY-TWO

THE FIRE PIT

I heard a knock at our door and I jumped out of bed just as it opened. Riadia and Peter had come to tell us that the village was meeting at the fire pit by the fountain and invited us to join them. Valdimer was still sound asleep. I suspected that he had spent too much time with the vodka jug. My attempts to rouse him resulted in a loud belch and a wave of his hand that clearly indicated that he wanted to sleep. I was anxious to see the rest of the village and meet it's inhabitants. With Riadia to interpret for me, I didn't need Valdimer this evening. I decided to let him sleep.

As Riadia and I walked toward the fountain I asked her to translate everything anyone said so I could fully participate in the meeting. She said she would do her best. I asked her what the meeting was all about and she responded that the village had a meeting every weekend on either Friday or Saturday night. In honor of our coming they decided to have the meeting tonight.

We walked a few steps past the fountain in the center of the village and just to the right of it was a small arena type circular fire pit. All of the villagers including their children were already seated there. The seats were four deep. The center was a flat area with a small fire pit in the middle. There were several dozen people sitting around the pit and a man was standing by the fire, talking to his audience. He was walking and talking, passing back and forth, sometimes in front of the fire, sometimes behind it. He used the fire for drama, appearing as just a shadow when he was in front of the fire and, when he was behind it, he glowed red, which he enhanced with wild facial expressions. He was telling a story to the village children that were all squatting in either the front row or sitting cross-legged on the ground in front of the first row.

Riadia led me down towards the front and everyone's big smile showed that I was welcome. The children slid over and made room for us on the front bench. The man was telling a story about a hunt that the village elders had participated in many years ago. They had tracked deer for several hours and finally were able to corner them near the King's hunting preserve. It was a delicate maneuver as they knew they would be shot by the King's guards if they killed deer inside the preserve. If the hunters shot deer outside the preserve it was fair game. The hunters were finally successful in scaring two deer out of the King's preserve. It was done by one hunter getting between the deer and the preserve. He made loud noises and the frightened deer ran away from the preserve, right into the ambush set up by the other hunters. They bagged two magnificent stags and brought them home to the Village. The storyteller described in detail the huge feast and celebration that lasted two days. The storyteller finished his story and turned towards two huge racks of antlers that were hung on the porch of the closest hut to the fire pit and told the children that those antlers came from the two stags that the hunters brought back.

The storyteller sat down and the children all clapped. Peter had set up a small bar with his crocks of Vodka, just outside of the circular pit. People in the crowd would go over with cups and fill them from time to time and as they did, they would throw a coin or two into a tin can that Peter had placed in front of his bar.

After we sat down, the next person to tell a story was Jana, Stanislaw's niece. Riadia sat next to me and kept me informed as to what she was saying. Jana's story was also for the children. Riadia whispered in my ear that the first stories were always for the children as they usually go to bed before the fire pit meeting is over. Jana started by talking about the beautiful golden grain that was coming up all around Lanski. She went into a crouch and in a sinister voice directed at the children said that you must be careful in the ripe golden fields, for dangerous beings move back and forth among the stocks of grain, waiting for small children. Wolves that eat children live in the grain fields. They are kept by the Rye Woman. She is a witch who is black and naked and helps her wolves capture children. Sometimes she captures children herself and carries them off to her underground home. She has the ability to become half woman, half beast and when she really gets angry, flames shoot out of her breasts. She is married to an old man with three heads who rarely leaves the underground home but on occasion he too lays in the grain waiting for little children. Jana reminded the children of being careful and warned them once again about the dangers lurking in the grain fields.

The children were visibly moved by the story and many of the little ones stared wide eyed at Jana and clung to their mother's or father's legs. Riadia explained as Jana sat down that the grain is so important to the health and prosperity of the village that these old Polish fables are told to keep the children from trampling down the new grain in their childhood games.

The next storyteller was Merzec and he told the children a story about how the Polish kings of old established their kingdoms. Riadia whispered to me that the children were getting a special treat tonight as Jana and Merzec were telling old Polish children's stories as much for me as for the delighted children.

Merzec began by gesturing with his arms, waving them in great circles, to emphasize that this story was about events that occurred long ago. He told the children that a thousand years ago two emissaries from God came to earth to select kings from all eligible inhabitants of central Europe to rule over the peasants. God would not consider selecting the king from the established royalty of Western Europe because "There was no virtue among the nobility."

There was a prominent peasant who had three sons and lived in the middle of the vast part of Europe between Germany and China. God had selected him as the father of his chosen king because of his honesty, integrity and high moral standards. God was unable to make a decision as to which of the three sons would make the best king because the father had raised all three to be perfect. When their father died, the three brothers, Lech, Czech, and Russ separated and traveled the known world. After ten years of wandering they all became homesick and, as if by a miracle, they all came home from different places and arrived on the same day. They met on a road and on seeing each other cried in one voice, "Pozanje," which is the Polish word for the phrase "I know you". On the spot they met, they built the city of Poznan which became the home of the kings of Poland for over five hundred years. The three brothers were selected by God to rule the area and eventually Russ became King of Russia, Czech became King of Czechoslovakia and Lech became the King of Poland.

One of the first things Lech did as king was to travel around Poland and select beautiful spots to build cities. He discovered in the dense southern forest a lush green valley that had huge trees around it. He ordered the trees cut down and when the workmen cut down the largest tree, a swarm of pure white eagles flew out of the tree. Lech was so overwhelmed by the sight, he named the white eagle the national bird of Poland. The city he built on the spot was the home of Krakus, a later King of Poland and the spot is now the city of Krakow. Merzec went on to say that when Krakus became king he moved his palace to Krakow. He established the "Kings Hunting Forest" near their home and for over 400 years it has been the best place to hunt game in Poland. He told the children that the forest still contains wild boar, deer, bear and many wolves.

He finished his story by telling the children to stay out of the King's Hunting Forest as it was also inhabited by the ghosts of former Polish kings and they would capture any children that strayed into the forest and feed them to the wild animals. By now the children had two scary lessons and they were all glad to be packed off to bed.

Aneskia was the next person to get up and speak, and she talked about how hard life was for her after her husband died. She talked about the war and how her husband had gone to fight the Germans in Warsaw and how he had been killed there. Everyone was listening but I had the feeling the story had been told many times before. I think that this time it was being told mainly for me.

This village forum served as their newspaper, television and radio. The village was so remote that they were completely cut off from the rest of the world's media. These weekly meetings were their only source of information and entertainment.

Aneskia went on with her story and described how as she got older, all she had left was the Stocowski family hut and her kind relatives that shared their food with her. She told the village about how cold she was in December and how her feet became frostbitten. She had run out of fuel and was thinking about going outside in the night and freezing to death as she had heard that once you started to freeze you didn't feel cold any more. She pointed at Riadia and said, "Our beloved Riadia saved me from that by telling me of a vision she had." This was the first time that the assembled villagers had heard the story, and they all leaned forward to hear what had happened.

As Aneskia told of the vision - that an event of international significance would change her life and the lives of her Stocowski relatives - there was an audible gasp from the crowd. She told how she had circled the date of December 6, 1966 as the date of Riadia's vision. Just today she said, she learned from Graham Taylor, (she pointed to me), that her long lost brother, Stanislaw, died in Seattle, Washington on that very day. The crowd again gasped and looked in wonderment from me to Riadia and then back to Aneskia. She pulled from her skirts the two rolls of Kennedy half dollars that I had given her and walked around the circle and gave one to the head of each household with the promise that they were good- luck charms. She said that Riadia had passed a blessing over them and they should never spend them. Everyone clapped and gave Aneskia a standing ovation. They all left their seats and either shook my hand or gave me a big hug. I thought the evening was over, but the villagers returned to their seats and began clapping and chanting, "KROTO." They were looking at me and then they all pointed at me and kept

chanting the word kroto. I asked Riadia what I was supposed to do. She responded, "Kroto, means story, and the
village wants you to tell them who you are and why you
have come to Lanski."

CHAPTER TWENTY-THREE

GRAHAM'S KROTO AT THE FIRE PIT

I couldn't refuse the crowd's request for a story. As a trial lawyer, I was used to speaking before full courtrooms, and this was a golden opportunity to bond with the village. I collected my thoughts and walked towards the fire pit. I started to talk, and the crowd immediately fell silent. They hung on every word. Riadia understood what I was saying and she translated my story to the attentive villagers.

I told of my days as a little boy going to Stanislaw's butcher shop. When I recounted the time I had traded one of Stanislaw's fresh ducks for a spoiled one, everyone laughed. I told of how he helped me cope with little problems as a teenager. When I explained about finding the money in an old footlocker and keeping it away from the Seattle Police they all gasped. They knew all too well that the police wanted to take custody of it.

I told them of "Dutch" Williams and my struggle to keep the money from going to the State of Washington. I talked about my struggle to find Lanski and of my trip to Warsaw. I told of Dr. Zeiss, and on mention of his name, one man in the crowd stood up and in a loud voice cheered,

"General Zeiss".

Riadia whispered to me that this man was Jana's husband and was called "Ivan the Warrior" by everyone in the village. At age 55 he was the strongest man in the village. He also served as head of the village and I soon accepted him as the "mayor" of Lanski. When Ivan was 33 he fought with General Zeiss in the battle to save Warsaw. When the Germans left, he came home and somehow avoided the blitzkrieg that destroyed Warsaw.

I was told later that he was the best friend of Aneskia's brother Paul. He had been like a brother to Paul since their early childhood. One morning in 1941 when Paul and Ivan were returning from a hunting trip, they found Riadia on the bank of the Wistula river near Poinki. She was suffering from a broken leg and if they had not rescued her, she probably would have perished. She indicated that Ivan was a wonderful man and she loved him as much as her adoptive father Paul. I asked her to explain further but she looked embarrassed and said she would explain in more detail when the time was right.

At that moment, I realized that this wasn't just a village; it was more like a clan or Indian tribe. Here was a group of people that lived together in total poverty with interlaced love for one another. I was swept away with the camaraderie of the villagers of Lanski.

I finished my story with my trip to Poinki and the visit with Father Patrick. As Riadia translated, several questions were asked. She translated that the people wanted to know if Father Patrick was going to re-open the church school. I answered the question by saying that Father Patrick seemed a little too much into the communion wine to run a church school. They all laughed as Riadia embellished the translation by staggering like she was drunk. The crowd agreed that most of the Polish priests ended up that way. My final words were about how we were attacked by a wild boar in the forest and how our car was stuck in the mud a few miles out of Lanski.

After answering the questions, I walked to the bench on the edge of the fire pit and sat down. Everyone applauded and then turned their attention to Ivan.

Ivan came to the center of the fire pit. He thanked me for my story and began to talk with sweeping arms and grand gestures. He spoke of the King's Hunting Forest and how sacred and protected it had been through the years of the monarchy. He spoke of hidden caves that contained bears, small valleys that protected herds of deer and forests that contained the fabulous wild boar that the village had cooked on occasional holiday feasts. It had been several years since the hunters of the village were lucky enough to catch a boar. He said that Lanski could have a spectacular wild game roast right here in this very fire pit if the men were willing to go back to the forest and look for the boar I had seen.

He challenged several of the village's young men, Peter included, to celebrate this great event with a hunt in the Kings Hunting Forest. The occasion of a lawyer from

Seattle, Washington, some 10,000 miles away, coming to honor and help their village, needed to be properly celebrated. He suggested that they leave immediately and by first light they could find the boar we had seen on our trip. He went on to say that Stanislaw was one of the only children born in Lanski that had gone out in the world to make his fortune. The fact that at his death he returned his wealth to his Lanski relatives was one of the finest tributes that any inhabitant of Lanski had ever paid to the village.

Everyone cheered and decided that we would have a great celebration tomorrow night with wild game from Ivan's hastily organized hunt. The hunters left the fire pit and went to their huts to get their gear. It was decided that they would leave as soon as they could load their wagon and hitch the horses. On their way to the King's Hunting Forest, Ivan said the hunting party would pull Valdimer's car out of the mud and make sure it was cleaned up and ready for our return to Warsaw, whenever we were ready to leave Lanski.

As we strolled back to hut number two, Riadia told me that the woods that used to be reserved for the former King of Poland and his guests were now open to anyone that wanted to hunt. She said she heard the men saying that the wild boar we saw would be easy to find as it obviously was protecting it's territory and would probably still be in the same vicinity. The men leaving for the hunt had asked me to explain exactly where we had the encounter with the wild boar. I recalled an outcropping of three giant boulders and a sharp curve in the road about a hundred yards from where we had stopped. Riadia told the hunters and they recognized the spot I described.

I asked Riadia how the men would proceed with the hunt. She said that the old method was to surround the boar but leave it enough room that it wouldn't charge. Then several men armed with spears would stand in a narrowed opening between rocks or trees and "beaters" banging metal cans together would drive the boar towards them. When the boar charged the men, they would throw a net over it and spear it to death. All the hunters were excited as they emerged from their huts and began assembling for the hunt.

I was amazed by the equipment they put together. There were a dozen or so 8-foot long spears with hooked guards near the pointed ends. Apparently that was so that the wild boar would get hooked on the guard if it was able to avoid the sharp point at the end of the spear. There was one old gun that looked to be 50 years old or more. Riadia said it was the only weapon in the village and that it was taken during a battle with the Germans many years ago. It looked like a World War I German rifle.

The hunters loaded a heavy cargo net and several primitive cymbals they had forged from the ends of 50-gallon steel drums. These were the noisemakers that the beaters used. All in all it looked like a stone-age hunt. I seriously doubted that we would have any wild game for a feast when the hunters returned.

By now it was close to midnight and I was exhausted and I said good night and retired to Aneskia's hut. Raidia told me to sleep as long as I could as the hunters would not return until noon or later. She said that that she and Aneskia would make lunch for Valdimer and me tomorrow. When I opened the door to Aneskia's hut, Valdimer was snoring so loud it made the room shake. I could not have cared less. Three shots of Vodka at the campfire meeting and the long day coming to a close made me so sleepy that I could have slept next to a ringing fire alarm. I collapsed on the feather bed and soon fell sound asleep.

CHAPTER TWENTY-FOUR

LUNCH AT PETER'S

It was about 8 a.m. when I opened my eyes the next morning. Valdimer was still asleep. I told him to get his butt out of bed and try and participate in the "Lanski experience." I told him he was on zero Vodka rations for the day if he wanted to be paid. He protested and I explained that "my interpreter" was too drunk to participate in last night's activities. He apologized and begged for forgiveness with such a humble attitude that I told him he was back on the payroll just to stop him from sniveling.

I heard a knock and opened the door. Aneskia was standing there with two homemade robes. She motioned to me like she was scrubbing her armpits with soap and threw the robes to me. I went back inside and said to Valdimer they were inviting us to bathe. We both threw our clothes on our beds and put on the robes. They were soft, probably knit out of cotton. We emerged from the hut and Aneskia herded us down towards the fountain. Beyond the fire pit which was still smoldering from last night's fire, was a small ledge that I had not seen before. Below the ledge, was a rock stall with a pipe coming out of the wall. Aneskia directed us into the stall, threw us a bar of soap and turned her back on us. The pipe led from an old tank under the fire pit. The village funneled water from the fountain through the fire pit and created a tank of hot water for villagers to shower in. We both stepped into the stall and saw two valves on the wall. One was warm water from the fire pit and the other was cold water from the fountain. It was primitive, but worked just like a normal shower. We finished and put on our robes. A few villagers were waiting for us to finish before taking their turn in the shower. I hoped we hadn't used too much of the hot water warmed by the fire pit. We went back to Aneskia's hut and I dressed in the peasant clothes I had bought in the outdoor market in Pionki. Valdimer put on his shirt and suit pants but left his suit jacket in the hut so that he could enjoy the warm sun.

It was about 70 degrees outside, but a cool breeze off the nearby mountains made it very comfortable. After we dressed, we came out of the hut into the warm, spring morning. Aneskia and Riadia met us and we followed them down to Peter's hut. We walked around to the rear of his home and entered a private patio that was surrounded by a lattice fence with grapes growing up the sides. We saw Konara, Peter's wife, whom I met last night. I introduced her to Valdimer, and they exchanged greetings. She was just finishing setting out an extravagant lunch for us on a long wooden table.

Konara seated us so that from our dining spot, we looked out over the Lanski valley. Our view was of 300 or so acres of wheat in the foreground with beautiful green mountains behind. The wheat was the mainstay of the village food crop. In the center of the valley we could see a beautiful crop of golden-brown wheat that looked much richer than the surrounding wheat fields. It covered 50 acres or so. Peter's wife Konara, proudly explained that the lush crop produced Peter's special grain used to make the village vodka. Apparently Peter was able to strike a proper balance for the village with the amount of wheat they needed for food and the amount of wheat he needed to produce vodka.

Konara placed two types of vodka on the table: One was spiced with berries and was a slight shade of red. The other was very clear and quite strong. Valdimer looked at me, begging for permission to sample Peter's vodka. I said "OK, Valdimer, enjoy yourself." He smiled an ear-to-ear grin and poured himself a glass of each type of vodka. He said to me with a wink, "I want to be polite and try them both."

Near the table was a small outdoor clay oven not unlike some of the pizza ovens I have seen in Seattle restaurants. Konara reached into it and produced several loaves of freshly baked bread. Then she moved over to a nearby oven-like stone fireplace. In its grate were smoldering embers from a much larger fire that must have been started several hours before. A large cast iron pot was in the center of the embers and its top was covered with what looked like green sod.

We all sat down and Konara lifted the pot off the embers and placed it on the table. She lifted the sod off the pot by pulling on a linen-like fabric that was between the sod and the food. Riadia said that the dish was "Prazonka" and was a one-dish dinner composed of potatoes layered with cabbage, thin sliced homemade sausage, pickles and goat cheese. There were pitchers of water and plates with warm fresh bread and fresh churned butter.

The meal was very special. The bread, Vodka, and Prazonka were wonderful and the flavors blended perfectly. The meal was particularly nice with our view of southern Poland wheat fields blowing in the background. It was clear why these villagers stayed here in the comfort of this little piece of paradise. Over lunch we talked about Lanski and it's inhabitants. Aneskia and Kanara talked about how much privacy they had enjoyed here compared with the rest of the country. Two world wars had been fought within 50 kilometers of their village, but Lanski was so lacking in importance that no foreign soldiers had ever entered the town. The communists who currently control Poland had never visited the village, and the villagers more or less conducted their lives as their ancestors had for hundreds of years. Konara reasoned that Stanislaw's money would help her family but she hoped it would not change their lives. She imparted some thoughts that I have relied on to this day. She said that they were happy and did not need anything from the outside world. The money which was more than anyone in Lanski had ever seen before, might make the children think of leaving the village and venturing out into the world. It was her worst fear and she hoped for the best. I told her that the money for her family and the rest of Stanislaw's heirs was for whatever use they wished. That seemed to reassure her, and as we finished off the fabulous Prazonka with a final glass of vodka.

After Lunch, Vladimer and I refilled our glasses with vodka and started a leisurely stroll through the village. Riadia joined us, and the three of us walked up the village main street and waved to all the villagers doing their daily chores.

The little boy I had put on my shoulders came out of a doorway and followed us about ten paces behind. From time to time I smiled in his direction and let him know I was glad to see him again. I motioned for him to walk with me. He very shyly came over and took my out-stretched hand. We walked hand in hand until we got to Aneskia's hut. He waved goodbye and ran back down the street. I never found out whose child he was. The children were taken care of by everyone in the village and it was hard to identify which children belonged to which parents.

As we were walking, I noticed that whatever work needed to be done was done as a village project. If a roof needed repair, everyone helped. If the walls of a hut needed cleaning, the neighbors on both sides helped. The older people couldn't do hard work but they helped with the smaller cleaning jobs. This resulted in the entire village being scrubbed clean daily. They even raked the dirt streets to give them a groomed look. It reminded me of the way groundskeepers at major league baseball stadiums rake the base-paths and pitcher's mound before ballgames. Lanski was as clean as a polished jewel.

Once back at Aneskia's hut, I got my briefcase and began making notes about my trip. So many things were happening, I wanted to keep a record so nothing would be forgotten when I returned to Seattle. Valdimer was taking a nap and after recording several pages of notes, I became drowsy and fell asleep as well.

We awoke to a large commotion going on outside. I opened the door and saw the villagers running up the road in the direction of the King's Hunting Forest. We joined the throng and as we jogged up the road, off in the distance, we saw the hunters coming down the road towards Lanski.

CHAPTER TWENTY-FIVE

THE HUNTERS RETURN

The village hunters had completed a great hunt. They had bagged a deer and two wild boar. The women hugged their men and dragged the wild game out of the wagons and headed towards the village. Peter was in one of the wagons and had a bloodied rag on his leg. One of the wild boar had grazed him in an attempt to get past him. I was concerned and told Riadia that I had some medicine in my briefcase. She passed this on to Peter and several of the men helped him into Aneskia's hut. I got some penicillin ointment I had in my shaving kit. The women washed the wound with soap and water and dried it with a clean towel. I dressed his wound with the penicillin ointment and covered it with a large band-aid I had in my briefcase. Everyone was impressed and Riadia said, "Now you are Dr. Graham."

Ivan and some of the hunters watched, and when Riadia explained what the antibiotic ointment could do, they raised their eyebrows in appreciation. I gave the rest of the tube to Peter with instructions on how to use it. He thanked me and went out to help the women clean the game. I asked Riadia if she could get the men to describe

the hunt. She whispered that the hunt story was tradition-
ally told at the feast. She said, "Each hunter will tell in
detail his part in the hunt as the villagers enjoy the feast. It's
part of the celebration and nothing about the hunt will be
missed."

The hunters were exhausted. They had not slept
since the preceding day and they all went straight to their
huts. Riadia said, "They are going to sleep until dinner was
ready, but don't worry, they will all be awake to share their
stories with us."

The women took over and hauled the game to the
fire pit. I went along to see how they would prepare the
game. The wild boars were gutted and washed clean. The
deer was skinned and trussed onto a long pole. The fire pit
from last night had been kept hot all day. I thought it
strange on an 70-degree day but remembering the morning's
hot shower, I thought it might be for keeping the village
hot water storage tanks full. I understood why the fire was
kept burning all day when I saw the women lifting red hot
rocks out of the embers. With large steel tongs, the hot
rocks were packed inside the cleaned out chest cavity of the
two wild boar.

They next uncovered a deep hole within the fire pit.
It had apparently been dug out earlier in the day in anticipation that the hunters would be successful. They placed
both boar in the pit, covered them with a heavy canvas tarp
and placed layers of sod on top. When I vacationed in
Hawaii in the late 50s, I saw the Hawaiians cook a pig for

a luau in much the same fashion. I knew how good it was going to taste.

The village women then turned to the deer. It was about the same size as our northwest deer, probably close to 150 lbs. The head and antlers were removed and placed on a steel spike that had been embedded in the ground outside the front door of the hunter that killed the stag. The fire pit was leveled to a bed of coals and two of the hunters helped set the pipe that the deer had been trussed to on a stand that stretched over the coals. The deer was bound to the pole with its legs stretched forward and backward so it looked like a big red sausage bound to the pole. As soon as the trussed deer was placed on the pole supports, the village children began turning the deer by the handles on each end of the pole. The trussed deer could be easily turned from both ends at the same time. It was the job of the boys to turn the deer while the girls gathered small wood chips to keep the coals burning hot. The older children used tin cups on long poles and basted the slowly turning deer with a rich honey-blackberry sauce. More hot rocks were prepared and about an hour later, the wild boars were uncovered and a second set of hot rocks were inserted in their body cavities to insure they were completely cooked.

Peter awoke early from his nap. When asked about his injury, he said he felt fine. He began bringing several crocks of vodka down to the area that was being set up for the feast. Apparently everyone in the Village owned the grain fields and this resulted in Peter's vodka being co-owned by Peter's family and the rest of the village. I sensed that the vodka making process was Peter's but about 50% of the vodka produced was Peter's and about 50% belonged to the village in exchange for the grain. Valdimer was visibly moved by the Village's cooperative efforts and told me he had never seen this type of community effort in Poland before this trip.

We sat by the cooking deer for several hours and watched the children and women of the village get ready for the celebration. About 5 that evening the hunters and their families began coming down to the fire pit. They were all dressed in colorful native costumes. Valdimer and I headed for Aneskia's hut to dress for dinner. We could hardly wait for the feast to begin. There was a sense of excitement and celebration throughout the village.

CHAPTER TWENTY-SIX

THE FEAST

Just after we returned to the hut, there was a knock at the door. When we opened the door, two teenage girls ran away giggling. As they looked back they pointed to some fresh clothes that were hanging on the side of the hut. The villagers were all wearing traditional festive peasant clothes and they had thoughtfully provided us with appropriate apparel for the feast. The costumes were colorful and very old. Valdimer and I went inside and tried the clothes on. Whoever picked them out had done a good job of size selection and both outfits fit. We emerged from the hut to find several dozen villagers that had assembled outside; as we stepped out into the evening sunset they all clapped and cheered.

We joined the crowd, arm in arm and walked towards the fire pit. A spot had been cleared and one of the men was playing an old accordion while several of the teenagers danced what could best described as half-Russian half-Irish Jig. The young men took turns doing a combination tap dance and Russian squat kick. Then the young women did some ballet-type movements. Riadia was there and she said these dances were always done by the young people and were handed down from generation to generation. Villagers continued to come from their huts and stroll towards the fire pit area. With everyone dressed in the old Polish costumes, they all looked like they were posing for a Travel Magazine photo shoot. Their pride and love for their Village was evident in everything they did.

Peter set up the bar with numerous jugs of Vodka. Everyone was trying some of his newer creations-including wild currant-spiced vodka, blackberry-spiced vodka and hot pepper-spiced Vodka. There were several other varieties as well. His regular, clear, high-proof Vodka seemed to be the most popular. I thought they all tasted great. The jugs of vodka were in plentiful supply and everyone was enjoying them.

Valdimer was particularly impressed, as he had never tasted vodka laced with natural flavors. He really liked the Hot Pepper vodka and thought Peter was a genius of a distiller. We both decided to visit Peter's vodka workshop before we left Lanski. For the next hour or two we mingled with the villagers and watched the youngsters dance. Valdimer was trying very hard to stay sober so he could translate for me if necessary. I told him to relax and have a good time.

Several tables were set up and the Women began filling them with food. They brought out fresh baked bread, butter and a variety of jams, jellies and honey. There were dishes of potatoes that were baked, fried, scalloped with cheese, and mashed with wild mushrooms. There were several vegetable plates of beets, a type of chard, and a spinach soufflé. Two young women brought pitchers of water and milk for the children. There were homemade pickles and other condiments and a variety of plates, napkins, and silverware, none matched.

The women took the deer off of the spit and uncovered the wild boars. The sod was stripped and the canvas pulled back exposing perfectly cooked boar meat. The cooks had added seasoning when they put the second set of hot rocks in the boars. The deer was also done to perfection. The blackberry-honey marinade that the village teenagers basted the deer with had crusted into a thick outer coating. I snitched a bite and it was like candied, smoked meat. When the venison was laid on the table the meat literally fell off the pole. The smells that drifted out over the crowd brought a chorus of oh's and ah's and everyone began to line up for the feast.

The villagers shared their plates and utensils, and I thought they might have trouble sorting them out and returning them to the proper owners when the feast was over. Riadia told me that they had done this so often that everyone knew exactly which silverware and plates belonged to each family. She brought a plate and silverware for each of us. We lined up and filled our plates with one of the best meals I have ever eaten. If I had to choose between the pork and the venison, it would be a difficult choice, but I think the blackberry-honey sauce poured over the deer on the spit for three hours won first prize. Peter's vodka would tie with the wild boar for second place.

During the dinner, the hunters stood up one by one and described the hunt. Ivan told first of leaving Lanski with the village rifle and a small amount of ammunition. They came to Valdimer's Messerschmit mired in the mud and everyone helped lift the little car up and out of the mud. The hunting party carried it over to solid ground and turned it around so it was headed back towards Pionki. He said they didn't want us to leave until we were ready but they wanted to help us on our journey home. Valdimer upon hearing this stood and bowed his thanks to the hunters.

Then Ivan told of riding the wagon toward the King's Hunting Forest. The sun had begun to rise in the east. As they neared the center of the forest they saw the luminous eyes of several wild boars staring at them from the edge of the tree line. The men got off the wagon and circled the area. Several men moved behind the boars into the trees. Those men were the beaters. They beat their 50-gallon drum lids together and made such a racket that the boars ran towards the rest of the hunters. They had the cargo net ready to throw on the wild boars, as they ran away from the beaters. There were three wild boars and they raced towards the trap the hunters had set for them. Two were netted and killed with spears thrust through the nets. One escaped by reversing its path and running back into the forest. In the process of running back through the beaters, the boar swiped Peter's leg with its tusk. Peter stood and described his part of the hunt and vowed to go back next week and get the boar that escaped.

One of the other men stood up and Riadia whispered that this was Stefan, the best rifleman in the Village. Stefan said that on the way back they saw a stag and a doe crossing the road. The village rifle was tossed towards him and he dropped the stag with one shot.

Ammunition was priceless and the hunters chose the best marksman to fire the gun. After he fired the shot, they recovered the spent shell casing so Stefan could reload it for future use. After Stefan spoke, each of the men that participated in the hunt told how they contributed to the kills. When the last had finished talking, the Village all stood and drank a toast to the hunters.

After dinner everyone gathered around the Fire Pit and more logs were put on the fire. The story telling began. First there were stories for the children, and then they were sent to bed. Peter set out more vodka as some of the village elders spoke of events long past. By now it was late in the evening. As the campfire died down the remaining audience asked Riadia to tell a story of her youth. At first she refused. It was obviously very painful for her to talk about her past. The villagers persisted and finally she asked me if I wanted to hear about how she grew up and the circumstances of why she was in Lanski. I told her that It would do me great honor to share her heritage with me and the rest of the village.

She nodded, staring at the hot coals for a few

moments - the flickering flame dancing in her dark eyes - then she stepped forward and faced her hushed, expectant audience.

CHAPTER TWENTY-SEVEN

THE GIFT

Riadia started her kroto with a lengthy historical background of her childhood years in Hungary. She spoke in Polish but repeated it in English for me. The following is what I learned from her at the fire pit that night.

Riadia's grandmother was the daughter of the gypsy king of the Kalderash clan and their home was the Burgenland. This is an area in Hungary, close to the Austrian border. Grandmother Talaitha knew of impending death in the older gypsies of the clan before they fell sick. She could foretell the sex of children months before they were born. She had the gift. Riadia's grandmother was a direct descendent of the Lovara and Kalderash clans. Her mother was the granddaughter of the gypsy king of the Lovaras.

Grandmother Talaitha married Riadias grandfather, Romi, In 1862. Riadia's grandfather was from a French part of the Kalderash clan that called themselves "Coopersmiths." Romi and Talaitha gave birth to Riadia's mother, also called Riadia, and she became the wife of one of the Kalderdash king's sons. Riadia's mother died at age 30 giving birth to Riadia.

Riadia was raised by her aunt with some guidance

from her father, but for most of her life, her father avoided her. She thinks he blamed her for her mother's death. Both of the clans of her heritage dominated the gypsy population of central Europe in the latter part of the 19th century. The Kalderash were a nomadic clan that moved from campsite to campsite in the Burgenland, but sometimes went into France or Austria. Riadia was born July 10, 1926 when they were camped near the Bakony Mountains about 150 kilometers southwest of Budapest in the eastern most part of the Burgenland. There were about 12,000 gypsies living in the Burgenland region when she was born. On the day Riadia was born, her grandmother, Talaitha died. Before she died, she summoned the clan to bring Riadia to her, and with a knife she made an X on each of their wrists and then bound their hands together. They stayed bound together until Talaitha died.

Riadia was told on her fourth birthday that this exchange of blood passed the gift from her grandmother to her. The gift of future sight was both a blessing and a curse. When Riadia was growing up, she could not only forecast future events but she could read the minds of the other children in the clan and know what her friends and playmates were thinking. When her father discovered this power, he used Riadia when he was buying and selling things. He exploited Riadia's gift because he wanted to know how much the buyers would pay and how little the sellers would take as they haggled over price.

From the moment she exchanged blood with her

grandmother, the gypsies of the Kalderash clan treated Riadia with a special respect. At a young age she was able to predict storms before they happened. Like her grandmother, she knew of impending death in the older gypsies of the clan before they fell sick. She could accurately tell the sex of children months before they were born.

In the spring of 1932, at the age of six, she told her father that they were going to be destroyed by the Germans and that the clan should be careful to stay away from Germany. One summer, while at their camp near Lake Balaton, they learned that the Nazi party had come into power in Germany. Riadia had a vision that these "Nazis" were the Germans that would annihilate the Kalderash clan. She told the elders of the clan of her vision. They took her seriously. Some panicked and sought the king's permission to leave Europe. Many went to join portions of the Kalderash clan living in England.

In the summer of 1934, Riadia's father took the remainder of the clan to Carpentras in southern France to attend a regional meeting with several sections of the Kalderash clan from other parts of Europe. The meeting was to determine how they should deal with the Nazi problem. The trek was memorable and took almost three months. Riadia had just turned eight and she remembered telling fortunes for the travelers and friends of the clan that she met along the way. Her father was always able to extract a few coins for her services. In no time the young gypsy's fame spread though the gypsy camps in Europe. At the meeting in Carpentras it was decided by the clan that they should avoid the Nazi influence in Germany and treat the Third Reich as their worst enemies. Riadia's clan returned to Hungary, fearing the worst. Their fears soon proved well founded.

The following year the Nazi party passed the infamous Nurenberg laws that designated gypsies and Jews as alien races. They were declared socially unacceptable to the Third Reich. The clan dwindled in numbers, many wishing to merge into the population of Hungary and avoid the inevitable. Riadia continued traveling with her father and the clan. She was able to prevent harm from coming to their family by warning the clan elders when she had visions of Nazi gangs headed for their camp, intent on burning their wagons and doing harm to them. They moved several times because of her visions and in every move it was confirmed that the empty campground was entered shortly after they left by a mob of torch or club-bearing Nazi troublemakers. Raidia turned from fortune teller to clan savior in the years from 1936 to 1939.

The Germans issued a preventative "Crime Control Order" in December of 1937 that classified the gypsies as potential criminals who needed to be regulated. Hungarian officials sympathetic to the Germans adopted the order as the law of Hungary. Over-zealous Nazi gangs of Hitler's youth movement raided the gypsy camps without fear of reprisal. If the gypsies defended themselves, they were killed on the spot and their wagons looted and burned.

The clan went into hiding in 1938 and early 1939. Then, in a matter of days, Nazi Germany defeated Poland. Hungary and Czechoslovakia soon followed and suddenly the clan was under the direct control of Nazi Germany. It was too late to escape. The Nazis began to hunt down the Jews and gypsies and had them classified according to their families. A Nazi general, Himmler, declared a system that all "zigiunier" (the German name for gypsy), must have identity papers.

Pure gypsies had brown papers, mixed-blood gypsies had brown papers with blue stripes, and non-gypsy vagabonds that were living with the gypsies had gray papers. It soon became evident that all those with brown identity papers were to be sterilized and sent to concentration camps. One day in 1939 a truck arrived in camp and several German soldiers got out with guns and herded everyone into groups. Riadia was just 13 and was shocked to be pushed around by a uniformed Nazi with a rifle and bayonet while her family was systematically inventoried. The Nazis seemed more interested in the young people. They lined everyone up and began to catalogue each and every gypsy according to name, place of origin and ancestral blood.

Riadia was determined to be of pure gypsy blood and accordingly was given brown identity papers. Everyone got identity papers and everyone was told they would be immediately sent to a concentration camp if they were not able to produce their identity papers when asked. She was separated from her family and friends for a few hours and then the Germans left as quickly as they had come. The Germans took several of the young men with them on various criminal charges and they warned everyone not to leave camp until further notice.

The camp lived in sheer terror for months waiting to see what would happen next. Then in June, 1939 an order was issued in Berlin that ordered all gypsies from the Burgenland with brown identity papers, to be shipped to concentration camps. The 12,000 Gypsies that lived in the Burgenland when Riadia was born had shrunk to 8,000. Riadia's father went to Dachau and most of the rest of her older relatives went to Buchenwald. None of them were ever seen again. She and several hundred of the younger gypsies were sent to Lackenbach near the Hungarian-Austrian border and were put to work building a new work camp. The camp was built especially to house young gypsies who could serve as slave labor for the Nazis.

They worked 18 hours a day and had to raise their own food. They were systematically sterilized to keep them from "breeding." Riadia was so young that she wasn't menstruating yet and the German's delayed her sterilization. As it turned out, she escaped sterilization because of the events that followed. Many gypsies died of starvation or committed suicide before the camp was finished. In November of 1940 the camp was completed and those who were still healthy became the first inmates. Within a few months there were about 2,000 gypsies in the Lackenbach camp and the Nazis used them as slave labor for anything the German war machine needed.

In the spring of 1941, Riadia was on a work party building a highway near the Czechoslovakian border directly north of Budapest. Twenty gypsies were taken by truck to the construction site and were told to bring enough food to last a week. They arrived at an old bridge crossing a small tributary of the Dunaj River. The bridge had been damaged by an explosion of some sort and could not support heavy vehicles. They were told to take off the damaged timbers, shore up the foundation, and repair the superstructure. They worked all day taking off the broken timbers with the primitive tools given them by the Germans. When night came they were told to make camp. Their German guards began to eat dinner.

Suddenly, without any warning, the German guards were attacked by a group of seven Russian aviators who were survivors of a plane crash. They were trying to get back to Russia and came upon the work party. They had been waiting to catch the German guards with their weapons down, and they got their chance when the Germans started eating. The Russians rushed the five German guards, a brief fight ensued and all five Germans were killed.

None of the gypsies or the Russians were injured in the brief fight. While the Russians were taking the German uniforms, they spoke to the gypsies in Russian and Riadia understood them. They asked if some of the gypsies wanted to accompany them across the front lines: They could pose as German guards with a gypsy work party. This would allow them to use the truck to get to the border much faster than walking. By traveling at night and using the German work order that was in the truck they could travel through road-blocks without arousing suspicion. They felt there would be no more than two checkpoints to travel through, and they could easily make the border by morning. Several of the gypsies volunteered when Riadia told them what was asked. The rest decided to leave for the mountain caves of Burgenland that were only a hundred or so kilometers southwest of their location.

Riadia and about a dozen of the work party loaded the truck with the German provisions and a 50-gallon drum of gasoline, and they got underway. Three of the Russians sat at the back of the truck, in German uniforms pretending to guard the gypsies. Two more also dressed as Germans, sat in the truck cab. The remaining two Russians, using borrowed clothes, blended in with the gypsy work party. With only a wave at the border, they crossed over into Czechoslovakia. The German uniforms, worked perfectly: The Czech guards waved them past a line of stopped vehicles. They were less than 100 kilometers from the border of Czechoslovakia and the Ukraine. They stayed on back roads and within a few hours passed into the Russian state of Ukraine. It was May 28th, 1941 and very early in the morning when they crossed the border. They had little resistance from two sleepy, Czechoslovakian border guards who were intimidated by five Germans pointing guns at them. Immediately after crossing the border, the Russians stripped off their uniforms. By the time they got to the first Ukraine check point they looked like Russians again.

The Ukraine officer in charge of the outpost greeted them as returning heroes and said they were lucky to get this far. The Ukrainians were expecting to be invaded by the Germans at any moment. They said the gypsies could not enter but the Russians could take them north to Russia if they immediately left the Ukraine. They agreed – everyone in the truck had become comrades, celebrating their escape, and the Russian airmen wanted to help the gypsies.

The Ukraine officer gave them a transit permit to travel across the western part of the Ukraine and into Russia. They traveled north, but by the end of the first day they had become hopelessly lost. They were driving in a German truck and everywhere they looked they saw the Ukrainian peasants packing their belongings to escape before the Germans came.

They went through abandoned farm after abandoned farm and without a map they had to rely on a compass. They stopped that night at an abandoned farm and found a storage tank full of fuel. It was very low-grade gasoline, and although it worked for a while, the truck engine eventually stopped. They were less than 20 kilometers from the Russian border so they decided to abandon the truck and walk. They camped for the night and at first light the Russian soldiers left them and headed north. The gypsies tried to follow but soon were separated. Several of the gypsies wanted to go due east but Riadia and six others chose north. The two groups parted and Riadia never saw the others again.

After walking for a day they lay down exhausted and spent the night in a farmer's field. On the morning of June 1, 1941 they woke to the sounds of German trucks and troops that had invaded the Ukraine. They were soon captured. They passed themselves off as local gypsies. They were herded into a holding area by the German troops. There were captured Ukraine peasants as well as several hundred Ukraine gypsies in the detention area. The Germans separated the gypsies from the peasants and told them they were going to a relocation camp in Chelmno, Poland. They were told that it was a special camp for gypsies only, and they would soon be re-united with their families.

Riadia had a vision that told her they would be murdered at the camp and she vowed to escape before they got there. They were trucked to a railhead and waited for a train. There were gypsies there, working for the Germans. They told the newly arrived gypsies of good food and pleasant working conditions at Chelmno. They kept telling everyone how lucky they were to be sent to this model camp for gypsies only. Riadia could read the gypsy traitor's minds and knew they were lying. They had sold out their own people in exchange for temporary protection. Riadia sent a chill through the lying gypsy who herded them on the train. She told him he was next: He would be dead by July. She had a vision of him being shot with the other traitors as soon as there were no more gypsies to ship off to Chelmno.

She tried to warn the gypsies that were still with her from the work camp, but none of them would give up the dream of going to a humane and safe "model camp." No matter what Riadia said, her vision was rejected as a young girl's paranoia. Everyone's spirits were high in anticipation of going someplace where they would be accepted. Riadia knew better.

They were put into 12 boxcars that were not totally enclosed. The Germans obviously relied on the lies spread by the traitors to convince the gypsy travelers not to try to escape. The wood slat sides on the boxcars were far enough apart for Riadia to slide between the boards. The train moved out towards Warsaw on the morning of June 4, 1941.

By mid-day they were passing near the King's Hunting Forest, southeast of Warsaw. Riadia decided to make her escape. Everyone in her car was sleeping, and there were only a few guards on the entire train. As they crossed a bridge over the Wista River, she slipped between the side rails of the box-car she was riding in and leaned out as far as she could. She saw an opening in the bridge's superstructure and jumped from the train, unseen. She landed in the swollen river and hit a rock breaking her leg.

After a desperate fight against the current, she

washed up on the south bank of the river. As she coughed up the water she had swallowed, she saw the train disappearing in the distance. She knew that she had vanished without anyone on the train knowing where she was. Riadia pulled herself up under the bushes on the riverbank, where she could not be seen and rested. She was in a very remote and heavily wooded area.

As night fell, she heard wild animals and other strange sounds nearby. Her gift told her that she was safe at last. The following morning, she was found by Paul Stocowski as he was returning from a hunting trip. He was with a young man who turned out to be Ivan. Just before they found her, Riadia had a vision that a man named Paul would find her. He was going to be her father as he had just lost his own daughter who was Riadia's age. When Paul approached her she looked at him and said "Paul, please help me, I have broken my leg. I have been sent here by divine province to replace your lost daughter. I am a gypsy girl escaping from the Germans and I have been waiting for you. Your name is Paul, isn't it?" Paul moved his finger across his forhead and made the sign of the cross, and tenderly picked her up. He splinted her broken leg, placed her in his wagon, and headed for Lanski.

Her leg never healed properly, but the village hid her from the Germans during the war and she was never bothered again. She concluded the story by saying that she confirmed after the war that the train she jumped from was a death train. The gypsies were loaded into trucks as they got off the train at the station nearest to Chelmno. The truck exhaust was rigged to go back into the part of the truck where the gypsies rode. By the time the trucks arrived at the camp, the gypsies were dead from carbon monoxide poisoning. Their bodies were dragged out of the trucks and dumped into mass graves. Chelmno was a giant cemetery. The Germans killed and buried over 5,000 gypsies at Chelmno.

Riadia had finished her story. Everyone clapped, and as the last embers in the fire pit were dying down, we headed to bed shaking our heads in disbelief at man's inhumanity to man. The memories of Riadia telling her story of survival would haunt me the rest of my life, and every time I hear of the holocaust atrocities I think of the poor gypsies who were tortured and murdered in the war. They seem to have been forgotten and ignored by World War II historians.

The Death Van in which the victims were suffocated by gas which was discharged from the engine. (The picture was taken after liberation of the town Chelmno by the Polish Army)[1].

CHAPTER TWENTY-EIGHT

PETER'S VODKA

We slept until nearly 9 the next morning. When we finally got up on that bright, sunny, Sunday morning we heard the birds chirping and no sounds of the villagers working in the fields. They were taking a day of rest from their usual hard work. We were prepared to start on our return trip to Warsaw, but we decided to visit Peter and see his amazing vodka factory before we left.

We dressed and walked down to Peter's home, going around to the back of his hut to where we had had lunch the day before. Peter's wife was hard at work in the outdoor kitchen. The door to Peter's vodka warehouse was open and we walked in. Peter was bent over, working on a still of some sort at a bench-like structure in the back of the storeroom. When we walked in, he immediately came over to welcome us.

We told him we were leaving shortly, but before we left, we wanted to learn his secret for distilling the smooth, high-proof vodka we had enjoyed during our stay in Lanski. He responded by showing us the grain he used. It was pure white and of very high quality. He also said that he distilled the fermented grain up to six times. He tasted it from the fourth distillation on and as soon as it tasted right, he would distill it one more time for good measure. He had been experimenting with various natural additives such as blackberry, honey and currant. He also tried hot peppers and mild peppers. On mention of the hot peppers, Valdimer smiled. I knew pepper-flavored vodka was his favorite.

Peter took us past a dozen steaming stills to his storage area and placed a small brown crock jug under the spigot of one of the storage tanks. With a wink he let us know this was his best vodka yet. He poured us each a small glass and told us to try it. At first it was tasteless, but when it reached the roofs of our mouths, it exploded. As it drained down our throats we felt like we had experienced a life-threatening event. Every organ in our bodies trembled as it went by. In a moment it was over. I had never experienced a totally pure alcoholic beverage like the 192 proof vodka Peter had just served us. He had distilled it six times and was considering a seventh pass through the still. He wanted our comments, but our vocal chords were temporarily paralyzed. When we could speak again, we said that we had never tasted better. To this day, that statement is true.

Valdimer wanted to buy some vodka and Peter agreed. They haggled over price and finally Peter smiled and said he would sell it for far less if U.S. dollars were the payment. I gave Valdimer three one-dollar bills. With them, he was was able to buy four one-gallon crocks of the 192 proof vodka. Peter then showed us some 192 proof vodka that he had mixed with hot pepper additive. Peter agreed to trade if Valdimer wanted the pepper laced Vodka. We tried some and it was half again as potent as the regular 192 vodka.

Valdimer decided to buy two of the jugs of the hot pepper vodka. Valdimer asked if someone would help carry the jugs to his car and Peter grabbed a couple of the teenagers who were hanging around the door to the storeroom. They were glad to be of help. They quickly picked up the jugs, put them in a hand cart with big wheels, and headed up the road to Valdimer's car.

We thanked Peter and strolled out into the center of Lanski to say goodbye to the friends we had made on our short stay. Valdimer, with his bald head and broad smile, looked like a totally different person than the man who had entered the village three short days ago. He was tan and looked ten years younger than when we first met at his brother's home in Warsaw.

Maybe it was the 192 proof vodka that we had consumed or maybe it was the stories we had heard. It didn't matter, we had bonded and as different as our cultures were, I accepted Valdimer as a friend who had experienced a phenomenal event with me.

We bade farewell to Lanski and waved goodbye to all the villagers who came out as we walked up the path that led to the Messerschmitt. Aneskia and Riadia walked with us. After several hugs they waved goodbye and returned to the village. I promised to send their inheritance to the U.S. embassy in Warsaw and told them I would research the most favorable exchange rate for them. Before we said our final goodbyes, Riadia told me, "I have a vision that you will meet your true love in a few years and have a beautiful blonde daughter." I was surprised and taken aback at this sudden prophecy from a gypsy fortune teller who didn't make mistakes.

CHAPTER TWENTY-NINE

BACK TO WARSAW

When we got to the Messerschmitt, I had to wrestle the keys away from Valdimer. He had been nipping on his vodka jugs while we walked. I got in and started the funny little car. Valdimer got in the passenger seat and soon fell fast asleep. I re-traced our path and the little car ran beautifully. After a few hours we neared Pionki. I thought about visiting Father Patrick, but we were running short of time and I decided against it. I planned to write him later and give him a full account of our trip to Lanski. Valdimer was sleeping like a baby as I pulled on to the road to Radom. There was little traffic and the driving was easy.

We reached Radom about 4 p.m. on Sunday afternoon. The town looked dead. I pulled into the same gas station that we used on our trip down. It had a closed sign out and there was nobody in sight. I had to beat on the door for five minutes before anyone appeared. The attendant came out and indicated with hand gestures that the station was closed. I waived five U.S. dollars and pointed to the Messershmitt. In an instant the owner was carrying a five-gallon can of gas towards the car. He promptly filled the car and the spare tanks. I gave him the five bills and two

Kennedy coins as a tip. He was a very happy gas station employee. The car was packed to the ceiling with vodka jugs; We must have looked like rumrunners. Valdimer slept through the stop for gas.

I started the little car up again and headed out on the highway to Warsaw. I remembered our route and drove directly to Dr. Zeiss's home. I pulled into his driveway about 6 p.m. and brought the little car to a stop.

Dr. Zeiss came out and embraced me. He went over to his half drunk, sleepy brother and shook his hand. We were all talking at once about what had happened to us on our trip. Dr. Zeiss said to me, "Let's hurry, you forgot that I had invited you to the opera tonight." I thanked Valdimer and paid him $200 more in small bills. He was very happy and told his brother how much fun we had on the trip. Dr. Zeiss cocked an eyebrow in the direction of all the vodka jugs and said, "I'll bet you had a terrific time." Valdimer beat a hasty retreat and I never saw him again. I was somewhat road weary but game to have a fun night in Warsaw with Dr. Zeiss. I used the guest room to clean up. The maid miraculously cleaned my suit while I was showering. She was just finishing ironing my shirt when I came out of the bathroom. I dressed quickly and went downstairs to find my host.

Dr. Zeiss had taken the 300 SL Gull Wing out of his garage and was warming it up in the driveway. He motioned for me to get in. I sat on the seat ledge and swung my legs inside. I then closed the overhead "gull-wing" door on the beautiful Mercedes sports car. Dr. Zeiss roared out of his driveway at 60 miles an hour. He swerved onto the main road and narrowly missed a small truck. The driver of the truck smiled and waived as if he was used to seeing the 300SL operated like it was in a road race.

The near miss made me realize that the neighbors were well aware of Dr. Zeiss's driving skills and kept their distance for their own safety. We headed for Warsaw at 90 miles an hour.

The Mercedes was the most exotic sports cars I have ever ridden in. It had a huge six-cylinder race engine that made a wonderful roar as Dr. Zeiss went through the gears. It hugged the road, and no matter how fast we took the corners, it simply curved around them with ease. It was a scary, fun ride – sort of like a thrill ride at an amusement park.

When we got close to my hotel, Dr. Zeiss cautioned me that there could be KGB agents waiting to ask me questions about where I had been. He told me to go to my room and drop off my briefcase and dirty cloths from the trip and come right back to the service entrance where he would be waiting for me. If I was longer than 15 minutes he would look for me.

Since it was Sunday evening, he said they might not be at the hotel this late. If they were there though, I would be detained for questioning. He said in a booming voice, "Graham, you have nothing to hide. You have done nothing wrong. Tell the truth."

I agreed, as all I had done was find the missing heirs of my deceased client. How could anyone fault me for doing my job? We were traveling at close to 50 mph and the hotel was not more than 200 feet ahead. He brought the 300 SL to a screeching stop at the back entrance of the Bristol hotel. He said, "Hurry, the opera is about to start." I thanked him for everything. Without him, my trip would have been a failure.

I grabbed all my belongings and hurried up the hotel stairs. I avoided the front desk and went straight to my room using the back staircase. There was no one in the hall and I didn't see anyone from the time I got out of the car until I unlocked my door and entered my room. For a moment I thought I was going to get in and out of the hotel without any hassle. Then I heard the buzz of the radio and knew they had been waiting for me.

CHAPTER THIRTY

KGB INTERROGATION

They wasted no time. I put my clothes and brief-case in the closet and heard a knock at the door. I opened it to find a man who identified himself as a Polish government employee. He asked me to accompany him. I told him I was going to the opera and didn't want to miss the opening act. He said, "I insist," and started to push me down the hall. I resisted and raised my hands in protest. Suddenly, two more men stepped in behind me. One was carrying handcuffs. I was roughly spun around and my hands were cuffed behind my back. I asked, "Where are we going?" They answered by pushing me into an elevator away from the regular elevators. The four of us barely fit in the small, dimly lit elevator. I started to panic. One of the men said, "Relax, Mr. Taylor, we just want to ask you some questions." One of the men pushed a button sending the elevator to the basement. The elevator came to a halt, and the doors opened to a dank, concrete hallway. The men steered me through a narrow doorway into a small room with a single bare light bulb hanging in the center of the ceiling. There was a small table and two chairs under the light.

The man who knocked on my door told me to sit down at the table. Suddenly, all my bags and clothes were brought in by another man. The handcuffs were removed and my interrogator said, "I am Henrich. I am a government employee assigned the task of keeping track of foreign tourists and their travels while in Poland." I asked him point blank, "Are you a KGB agent?" With a sly smile he answered "Yes." Henrich spoke perfect English. I complemented him on his English and he said, "I was educated at Columbia University in New York under an exchange program. Unfortunately, I lost track of you for several days and my superiors are concerned that I am not doing my job." He pulled out a pocketknife and began cleaning his nails. Suddenly he stabbed the knife into the middle of the table a few inches from my hand and in a loud voice said, "WHERE HAVE YOU BEEN FOR THE LAST THREE DAYS, MR. TAYLOR?"

I was prepared for this question, but not for the way it was delivered. I calmly took the knife out of the table, folded the blade back into the scabbard and handed it back to Henrich. I quietly told him that I was traveling in southern Poland looking for the long lost heirs of my deceased Washington client, Stanislaw Stocowski. Henrich narrowed his eye and demanded, "Why didn't you ask for help from my Government?" My briefcase was near the table and, with his permission, I picked it up, opened it and got out the part of the estate file I had brought with me. I showed the numerous letters I had written to the Polish government – all of which had either gone unanswered or were answered with form letters that were of no help. He took particular interest in the Polish Postal Service stamp that had returned my original inquiry because I had spelled Warsaw wrong. He said, "The arrogant postal workers must stop this foolish misguided national pride or Poland will never get out of the stone-age."

Henrich asked me whether I had taken any photographs on my "vacation to Southern Poland." I told him I had checked my camera in at the front desk, adding, "I was worried about being robbed." He barked a command and one of the guards left the room. He was back in a minute or two with the camera that I had checked several days ago in the hotel safe. It was still on it's first frame. I picked up my camera and said, " I will take some snapshots of Warsaw now that I have returned."

I looked at my camera and then in a rash move said "smile" and snapped a flash shot of Henrich. He grabbed my camera and pulled out the film to expose it. With obvious anger he said, "Stupid moves like that could put you behind bars for a long time while my staff thoroughly investigates everything you have done in Poland." I apologized and told him I just wanted to demonstrate that it was a real camera. He set my camera down and picked up my wallet and passport purse. He rifled through them finding only a few business cards and several hundred zloty. He demanded a receipt for the Zloty and I was able to produce the one given to me at the airport.

Just then Dr. Zeiss burst into the room and demanded to know why his dinner guest was being detained. Henrich jumped to his feet and saluted and in a mouse-like voice said, "General Zeiss, I did not know that you were waiting for Mr. Taylor. My conversation with him is over and I hope you enjoy your evening."

Henrich thanked me for answering his questions and said all my belongings would be in my room when I returned. He acted like we were just having a friendly chat. He went so far as to put his arm around my shoulder and thank me for explaining the estate matters to him. I had the chilly feeling that without the intervention of Dr. Zeiss, I would have spent many hours in the basement interrogation room. In retrospect, I realize that during this period in our country's history the FBI was probably doing the same kind of foolish interrogation of Polish tourists in America.

As we walked out of the room and took the stairs to the lobby, Dr. Zeiss winked at me. I was a sweaty mess and he kindly gave me his handkerchief to wipe the sweat off my forehead. He led me through the lobby and out of the hotel. We got in the Mercedes that he had parked in front of the hotel and went straight to the Opera House. Dr. Zeiss pulled the 300 SL into a driveway alongside of the Opera House. We were waved past a check point by an armed guard and parked in a small lot reserved for patrons of the opera.

We slipped in a side door and took an elevator upstairs to a small bistro. There we had a light supper of toast points covered with caviar and smoked pheasant, a fine French Chardonnay, and cold white Borsch. The wine was excellent. The first I had tasted in Poland.

There were 30 or 40 men in the room. Not a single woman except for kitchen help. The men were all in dark suits, tuxedos or cut-away tails. Shortly we heard a soft bell followed in a few minutes by several louder bells. Dr. Zeiss led the way to our seats. The bistro was very close to the box that Dr. Zeiss shared with one of the men I had met. We entered just as the orchestra was warming up.

The Opera House was larger than Carnegie Hall. I estimated that it housed close to 10,000 people and every seat was occupied. Our box seats were so close to the stage that I could have easily chatted with a performer in conversational tones. The box was just above the stage and below what is referred to as the "Dress Circle." We were on the right side of the stage and had an excellent view of both the stage and the audience.

When we first entered the box, Dr. Zeiss was greeted by a standing ovation from the entire crowd. He waved to the audience and then in a sweeping gesture swung his arm towards me and began clapping. 10,000 people joined in and I felt compelled to bow. It was quite an experience attending the Polish opera with a local "god." Dr. Zeiss arranged the red velvet privacy curtains on each side of his box, so that we were not so visible to the audience. I noticed there were a few women in the audience. I mentioned to Dr. Zeiss the presence of the women and he remarked that they were tourists. Dr. Zeiss explained, "The tickets are too expensive to waste on women." I often thought of those comments during the woman's equal rights movement in the United States. I wondered how many years passed before Polish women got to visit the opera house as anything more than cleaning ladies.

The Warsaw Opera House

CHAPTER THIRTY-ONE

AIDA

The house lights dimmed and as the curtain went up a waiter magically appeared with a small table, two glasses and a bottle of Belevedere Vodka. Dr. Zeiss reminded me that this was the finest vodka in the world. I agreed that it was very good, but I secretly thought that it couldn't hold a candle to Peter's best. We toasted each other and sat back to watch the Polish production of Giuseppe Verdi's "Aida."

Verdi's opera "Aida" is set in Egypt at the time of the Pharaohs. It is a story of lust, war and betrayal. (My kind of opera.) The commander of the Egyptian army is Radames. Amonasro is the king of Ethiopia and the enemy of Egypt in general and Radames in particular. King Amonasro's daughter is Princess Aida. The Ethiopians are invading Egypt.

In a battle that occurs before the setting of the opening act, Aida is captured and enslaved as a prisoner of war and sent to Egypt. She was housed in the Pharaoh's palace, befitting her royal status, and while there Radames falls in love with her.

This upsets the Pharoah's daughter, Princess Amneris, who is also in love with Radames. After a love scene with Aida, Radames leaves to defend Egypt from the Ethiopian invasion. He wins the battle and returns to Egypt triumphant, with the spoils of his victory and many Ethiopian prisoners, including King Amonasro, Aida's father.

The Ethiopian King, now a prisoner, re-unites with Aida in prison. He realizes that she has Radames under a lover's spell and convinces Aida that she should get Radames to tell her of the Egyptian battle plans. She agrees and Radames gives the details of the Egyptian battle plans to her to win her favor. Radames thinks that, as prisoners, Aida and Amonasro can do nothing with the information. The Pharaoh's daughter, Princess Amneris, uncovers the espionage and tells her father. Radames is sentenced to death by being buried alive in an Egyptian tomb. Aida joins him and they die in each other's arms. As they are singing their final song, Amneris is praying on the top of the tomb lamenting her betrayal of the man she loved, which resulted in his being sent to his death.

The production was spectacular. The stage was five stories tall with elevators that lifted huge pyramids, live elephants, camels and lions onto the stage for various scenes. The battle scenes were incredibly realistic, even from 30 feet away. When a warrior was stabbed, real blood-like fluid gushed out of what looked like a real wound.

Dr. Zeiss gave me a running commentary on the

opera and kept pouring vodka throughout the performance. I nodded off to sleep in the last act and Dr. Zeiss kindly nudged me so that I could see the finale.

When I awoke, Dr. Zeiss covertly pointed towards the back of the opera house. I saw Henrich standing at the back looking directly at us with opera glasses. When he saw I had spotted him he lowered the glasses and gave me a grim smile.

I turned my attention back to the opera and was soon caught up in the grandeur and emotion of the finale. As the last note of the opera faded, the audience rose to it's feet as one with thunderous applause. There were seven curtain calls. On the final call, as soon as the curtain came down for the last time, Dr. Zeiss pressed a buzzer near his seat and three men came from behind the stage curtain and opened a small door on the edge of Dr. Zeiss's box. They folded out a small three or four step staircase leading to the stage. I chanced a glance back to see if Henrich was still watching me, but he was gone.

With a fresh bottle of Belevedere vodka in his hand, Dr. Zeiss led me to the stage. In a moment we were back stage mingling with the performers and passing around the vodka bottle. Long tables laden with food appeared and the opera company began a celebration of their triumphal performance. We enjoyed the cast party for about an hour and then went back to Dr. Zeiss's car. He was not affected in the least by all the vodka he had consumed. His gait was steady and his speech had no trace of a slur. I did the best

I could to act the same as my host. We briefly discussed Henrich and Dr. Zeiss said, "Graham, don't worry, you have done nothing wrong. He probably just used you as an excuse to watch the opera without paying for admission."

He dropped me off at the front door of my hotel, which was just a few blocks from the opera house. He promised to meet me in the morning as he knew I still had to locate one last heir, Dr. Edward Stocowski. I entered the hotel with some trepidation, expecting to be dragged down to the cellar again for more questioning. To my relief, I was ignored by everyone I passed on the way to my room.

I opened the door to my room and found all of my belongings had been carefully stacked on the bed, including my camera with a fresh roll of film. Perhaps Henrich was making amends for his clumsy interrogation.

I fell asleep humming the aria from Aida that was my favorite, "Celeste Aida."

CHAPTER THIRTY-TWO

EDWARD STOCOWSKI

D r. Zeiss called me on the hotel house phone at 8:00 a.m. and in a booming voice said "It's time to get up you lazy Yankee." I laughed and said I would be right down. I dressed quickly and in a few minutes was in the lobby. We had a hurried breakfast in the hotel coffee shop and then left for Dr. Zeiss's hospital.

Once at the hospital we went to his office where I was warmly greeted by his assistant Monica. Dr. Zeiss excused himself, saying that he had to make hospital rounds. He said, "Monica will help you. If she can't find Edward Stocowski, nobody can."

Monica started by calling the university administration office and asking whether there was an Edward Stocowski on the faculty. They said that indeed there was and asked, "Who wishes to speak with him?" Without responding to their question, Monica asked to speak to Edward Stocowski's supervisor. In a few minutes she was talking to one of the University of Warsaw's department heads. After a few seconds of conversation she hung up and smiled. She said, "Dr. Stocowski will be here in Dr. Zeiss's office in an hour."

She had told Edward's boss that Dr. Zeiss wanted Dr. Stocowski in his office immediately to discuss some important matters of State. She sent Dr. Zeiss's Zim to pick him up. He would arrive by 10:00. I marveled at her efficiency and the ongoing ability of Dr. Zeiss to get whatever he wanted in Warsaw. She took me into Dr. Zeiss's office and gave me some magazines to read. She reassured me that as soon as Dr. Stocowski arrived, she would summon Dr. Zeiss and we could have a conference.

I busied myself making notes about the events of the last three days and took stock of my remaining cash. I wanted to give some small bills to Edward and was worried that I didn't have much left. However, when I looked in the money compartment of my brief case I found a wad of $50 bills, a stack of $20 bills, about $300 in ones and fives, and two thousand in $100 bills. That, with the few hundred in my wallet, would be plenty.

I heard a commotion in the reception room and I opened the office door to see a man standing in front of Monica's desk. She was calling Dr. Zeiss and in a minute she reached him and told him to come back to his office. Then in English, she said to me, "This is Edward Stocowski," and turning to Edward said, "This is Graham Taylor from Seattle, Washington."

I smiled and extended my hand and he spoke to me in broken English. He didn't know why he had been summoned and was frightened. His legs were shaking so badly, I thought he might fall down. He was perspiring heavily and his shirt was soaking wet. Sweat was beading up on his chin and on his forehead. I put my arm around his shoulders and reassured him, "You are here for a pleasant surprise. Don't worry." He smiled nervously and followed me into Dr. Zeiss's office. He had a striking resemblance to a popular singer and movie star of the time, Mario Lanza.

In a few moments, Dr. Zeiss came in a side door and went over to shake Edward's hand. He said in his loud voice, "You are a very lucky man. This is my friend from Seattle, Washington, Graham Taylor. He is a lawyer from the United States of America. He brings you news of the death of a long lost uncle of yours, Stanislaw Stocowski, that you probably never knew existed. Your uncle Stanislaw died in Seattle on December 6, 1996 and left you part of his estate. Mr. Taylor met me in Seattle earlier this spring and I agreed to help find his deceased client's relatives. This is why I summoned you to come to my hospital." With that he hugged Edward, congratulated him and left as quickly as he came.

Edward took in every word, and as the reason he was brought here sunk in, a larger and larger smile spread over his face. He never said a word while Dr. Zeiss was talking, but after Dr. Zeiss left, I couldn't stop Edward from talking. He wanted to know everything about his Uncle Stanislaw and how I became his lawyer. I spent the next hour going through the entire file and sharing with Edward all of the events of my visit to Lanski.

He was especially interested in the success of Peter's

vodka production. He said that the distillation of vodka was a skill passed down through generations. Only one man in the village was designated as keeper of the village vodka stores. He was impressed that this honor had been bestowed on Peter. He confessed that after his father died, he ran away from Lanski and came to Warsaw to work. He educated himself by going to school at night and had been improving his education for the last fifteen years.

He had not been back to Lanski since he left almost sixteen years ago. I brought him up to date on everyone in his family and what they were doing. He promised me that he would go back in the next week or two and spend a weekend with Peter and his family. I then went into detail about his inheritance and offered him an advance of $1000 in small U.S. bills. He gratefully accepted the stack of bills and told me this was the most money he had ever accumulated at one time in his life. This $1000, when exchanged for Zloty at the 2000 to one rate, would pay for his apartment and food for over a year and would allow him to travel on university-sponsored seminars in neighboring countries.

He said he had always wanted to go to the annual oncology seminar in Geneva, Switzerland, that was held in September of each year. This would be the first year he could afford to go. He was in oncology research at Warsaw University Medical School. His field of study was expanding by leaps and bounds with each passing year and he was missing out on continuing education. He had already exhausted Warsaw's educational resources available in his field of study.

Access to money for travel would allow Edward to take his career beyond being just another minor medical official at the University of Warsaw. I thought to myself, "This money from a butcher in Seattle might make the difference in a cure for cancer." Edward was visibly moved by his sudden prosperity. He said he was going to concentrate on becoming the best oncology research scientist in Europe. He indicated that he would probably leave Eastern Europe and seek a research position in the west because he believed that was where future breakthroughs in oncology would come from.

We talked about transferring the rest of his money to him and he indicated in no uncertain terms that he didn't want another penny of it to ever come into Poland. He begged me to pick a good bank in Seattle and open up a trust account in his name. Edward said he would come to Seattle sooner or later to collect it. He asked how much I would charge to maintain a trust account for him and I said I would do it for $50 a year. He said, "Done." He signed a hastily drawn trust document on one of my yellow pads that would allow me to keep his money safe in a trust account until he came for it.

We then spent some time talking about Stanislaw's life in Seattle and of Keiko and her many years of taking care of Stanislaw. Edward wanted to meet her when he got to Seattle. Next he offered to take me to the university and show me his research and I accepted. He also invited Monica and Dr. Zeiss (who had just returned), to join us, but they both declined. Monica arranged for the Zim to take us back into town.

I realized that I probably would not see Dr. Zeiss again before I left Poland. I thanked him for his help and his hospitality. I said, "My trip would not have been successful if it hadn't been for you. You must stay with me on your next trip to Seattle." He embraced me and then vigorously shook my hand and said in his booming voice, "I know we will meet again. I thoroughly enjoyed the time we spent together." Just then a bell sounded and he dashed out the door with a final wave goodbye. Monica said, "Just another routine emergency he needs to attend to. We have several every day." I took her hand and thanked her warmly for all her help. Edward with a twinkle in his eye, also thanked her and suggested that they get together soon to have lunch. She blushed and said that she would enjoy that very much. Just then the Zim driver came in and announced that the car was ready. Edward and I left Dr. Zeiss's office and headed for the front entrance. Outside was the brightly polished Zim waiting for us. Edward remarked that he had seen these vehicles around Warsaw but this was the first time he had ridden in one.

The Zim sped us through the Polish suburbs and as we passed the old-looking buildings I remarked to Edward, " I am amazed that these buildings are less than 25 years old. I can scarcely believe that Warsaw is actually a re-built city." I told him about my discussions with Dr. Zeiss and the Clemshaws at the U.S. Embassy about the way the Nazi's destroyed Warsaw. Edward said "It wasn't all destroyed, let me show you the part that was saved. We can have our lunch later."

He spoke to the driver and the car turned East. The Zim headed across the Vistula River and on the eastern side we passed through Washington Circle and drove into a section of Warsaw I had not seen before. Edward said, "We call this area Praga." It was as if someone had turned back the clock 100 years.

Limousine of Dr. Zeiss

Praga's Astronomical Clock

CHAPTER THIRTY-THREE

PRAGA

The buildings were very old and the inhabitants looked like the old brown and white photographs my grandparents kept in their attic. Edward explained that this was where the Russian Army camped when the Germans were destroying Warsaw. The Germans who returned to destroy Warsaw left the Russian encampment alone because of Stalin's secret pact with Hitler. The area was a section of Warsaw that survived the war without any damage.

The shops, bars and the dress of the people on the streets was as if time had stood still. The clothes being worn by the residents looked like they were right out of an old silent Charlie Chaplin film. They contrasted sharply with the attire worn by the many tourists visiting the area. Edward said, "This historical district is really the genuine, Old Town, unlike the one full of tourist shops near the main square. The Polish government gives special tax breaks to the inhabitants that dress in historical costumes to give the district a distinct historical look." The buildings had the same architecture as the ones in the re-built part of Warsaw, but they were obviously much older as shown by the worn down cobblestone streets, sidewalks and masonry.

Everything was extremely clean. There were several people washing down the sides of the buildings with soap, water and long handled brushes.

We came upon a large square in the very center of Praga where there were hundreds of open-air stalls filled with people buying and selling everything from gold bars to tooth paste. We stopped the car, and as we got out, Edward cautioned me to be careful of pickpockets. He said, "There were no police in the market. It is run as the only public market in Warsaw that allows the people to engage in free commerce. Money exchange laws, forget about them. No police, no problems. This is where all Warsaw comes to buy, sell and exchange foreign or banned goods."

Edward went on to say, "The market is full of thieves and pickpockets. The only police or KGB agents in the market are here buying or selling their own goods." All the rules were off in this picturesque old world public market. This type of barter and exchange must have been going on here for hundreds of years. I was surprised to see western TV sets, radios and electric appliances. The goods were priced in zolty but nobody paid the asking price. I thought of Riadia and how handy she would be in this market. I noticed a lot of food and vegetable stalls selling meat, produce and fish products that I had not seen before in Poland. You could buy anything from Mexican jumbo shrimp to California artichokes in this market. The exotic foods were very expensive, but there were well-dressed patrons with full grocery bags leaving the food stalls. Even in Warsaw there were the haves and the have-nots and this market scene was full of both.

We strolled among the shops and I stopped at the stall of a rare coin dealer who was selling real United States $20 gold pieces. I had priced them in Seattle before I left and they were about $200 each. Here they were selling for face value, but it had to be in U.S. currency. I asked the vendor if he would discount the coins if I bought several. He agreed to sell me six for $100.00. in U.S. currency. Since I was exchanging U.S. money for U.S. money I decided that there probably was no risk and with Edward helping in the bargaining, I made the trade. I should have bought more as I sold them several years later for $800 each.

We went deeper into the market. Dr. Zeiss's driver came with us and acted as sort of a bodyguard. We saw Russian soldiers selling Beluga caviar for $1 a tin. I asked Edward if he would spend some of the money I gave him on my behalf and I would credit whatever he spent to his account in Seattle. He was happy to oblige and I bought ten one pound tins of Beluga caviar for ten $1 bills. We passed tables where merchants were selling diamonds, emeralds and rubies. They were cheap, but I didn't have the ability to properly grade them and accurately determine their worth. Some of my jeweler friends at home would have been in heaven to be able to bargain with the jewelry merchants in the Praga market.

We passed a section of the market that had all of the

cut crystal that I had seen in the government shops in Old Town. There were several merchants all claiming their crystal glassware was better and cheaper than their neighbors'. The crystal could be purchased for less than 10% of the prices that were being charged in the government shops in Warsaw.

I bought several vases and a set of 36 crystal wine glasses in various sizes. With Edward's help I was able to bargain and pay about half of what the merchant wanted for the crystal. My entire purchase cost less than $24.00 in U.S. currency. By now, we had bought so much that we decided to return to the Zim. We were all loaded down with the purchases. Our visit to Praga was one of the highlights of my trip to Poland. My only concern at the time was how I was going to carry the crystal home to Seattle, without breaking it. Edward said that there was an American Express office back by my hotel and they would ship it to an American Express office in any U.S. city of my choice.

When we got in the Zim with all our packages, Edward said, "Graham what would you like for lunch?" I replied, "Edward, I want to treat you to lunch at your favorite restaurant." Edward told the driver to take us to the Victoria Intercontinental. It was about 3:00 and we were right at the height of the dinner hour. The residents of Warsaw ate a large mid-day meal and a light supper. Although it was a late lunch by my standards, by Warsaw standards it was prime time for the day's main meal.

We stopped in front of the Victoria Continental and headed for the restaurant. Our driver stayed with the car and was allowed to park the shiny Zim right in front. Alighting from such an elegant limousine gave us celebrity status as we entered the restaurant. With bows and scrapes we were shown to a small alcove and a table set with white starched linen. The lunch was a fixed price meal with everything included. A bottle of vodka was brought to the table and a waiter in a tuxedo wheeled up a tray of appetizers on a black lacquered cart.

There were four or five different presentations of caviar, some smoked trout or salmon, and some pickled fish. Our selections were skillfully put on plates and placed in front of us by two waiters dressed in tuxedos. As they wheeled away the cart, we sipped our vodka and enjoyed the appetizers we had selected. We chatted about Lanski, the open market we had just come from, and I told Edward some stories about life in Seattle. As we finished the appetizers, one of the waiters returned with a plate of steak tartar, which I later learned was a specialty of Warsaw's fine restaurants. The tartar was garnished with lemon wedges and toast points. It was excellent and we soon finished it.

Next, the waiters brought to our table, two platters covered with large silver covers. They placed one platter in front of each of us and, with a flourish, lifted the covers off in unison and banged them together with a loud clang. It was most impressive and apparently a trademark of the Victoria Intercontinental. The meal was roast veal with small new potatoes that were French-fried. The meal was complemented with green spinach and fresh warm sweet rolls. After the main course, the waiters returned with a dessert cart containing pastries, cakes and éclairs. The éclairs looked so special I took two. Edward selected a piece of cake and a pink sugar coated French pastry. The waiters poured each of us a cup of espresso. I had come to accept espresso as the only available coffee in Poland, with the exception of the home of Dr. Zeiss.

When we had eaten the last morsel of dessert we called for the check. The waiters brought us a bill for 200 Zloty. I pulled out a U.S. $20 bill and put it in the payment wallet. At first the waiters were afraid to take the U.S. currency, but with some kind words from Edward, the head waiter pulled some money out of his own pocket and slipped 200 Zloty into the payment wallet. He discreetly slipped the $20 bill into his pocket and with excessive bowing and scraping followed us all the way to the door. Edward thanked me for lunch and said, "Next time it's my turn." He went on to assure me there would be a next time, more likely than not in Seattle.

CHAPTER THIRTY-FOUR

THE ATLAS

After lunch, we went back to the Zim and Edward directed the driver to take us to the American Express office where I could mail my glassware home. I was happy to learn that there was no duty on Polish crystal. It cost $50 to send it to the American Express office in downtown Seattle. It was a relief to be rid of the heavy packages.

I got back in the Zim and Edward announced that he was going to show me Warsaw University. He did his undergraduate work there before he got into Warsaw Medical School. I wasn't sure why we were going back to his undergraduate haunts, but I sensed that there was something there that he wanted me to see. On the way we passed a beautiful church that was named "The Church Of The Holy Cross." It was baroque in style and of course, Catholic. Edward was a practicing Catholic and he said, "This is the church I attend. Would you like to see the most beautiful church in Warsaw?" I responded that I would and our driver immediately pulled over in front of one of the most beautiful churches I had ever seen. It reminded me of St. Patrick's in New York city. We walked up the front steps and went inside. The interior of the church was bright and cheerful and in the center behind the alter was a statute of the Virgin Mary. To her right was a cross with Christ imposed on it in crucifixion.

Edward pointed out that in Poland the Catholic figure most worshipped is the Virgin Mary. The Polish custom is for her to occupy the position of honor behind the alter, facing the congregation. He said that the long history of suffering by the Polish led them to adopt the Virgin Mary as a symbol of hope and salvation, rather than the redemption message which is central to the traditional worship of Jesus Christ. The Catholic church was not recognized by the Polish government, but it was still a part of the lives of many of the inhabitants of Warsaw. We made a small donation on our way out of the church and continued on our way to Warsaw University.

We entered Warsaw University through a gate reserved for faculty. Our driver pulled into a faculty parking lot and Edward told him to wait. Edward said that he was a graduate of the geography division of the university and he taught mapmaking classes at Warsaw University two nights a week. The map classes brought in just enough extra income for him to get by. He said, "I help make maps for the Polish and Russian government, and am regarded as one of the best map creators that the university has ever produced." He went on to say that he almost became a full-time professor in the geography department of the university before he was accepted into medical school.

We visited several classrooms where the teachers

nodded in recognition of Edward. It was obvious that he was well known and apparently well liked by the faculty and students. Our tour ended in a basement storeroom where Edward searched for something he wanted to give me. After a few minutes he produced two wrapped packages, handed them to me and with a proud smile said, "Don't open these in your hotel. It's better you don't know what is in them. I participated in making these and they are truly works of art. Take them to your embassy and they can arrange to have them shipped home to you. I know you will enjoy them." Apparently, he had given me a world atlas that he had helped produce. He wanted me to see what an accomplished mapmaker he was. I sensed that the atlas may have some strategic value, and in cold-war Poland, he was just being careful.

I thanked Edward for his kind gift. After the unpleasant visit from Henrich last night, I decided that my next stop would be the U.S. Embassy. We got back in the Zim, and at my request, Edward directed the driver to take us to the U.S. Embassy. Edward dropped me at the Embassy with my packages and said good-bye. He told the driver to take him to the hospital where he worked. His last words to me were that he would reluctantly send the car back to Dr. Zeiss before he got too attached to it. I laughed and told him I would look forward to our next meeting in Seattle.

I entered the embassy's side door carrying the gifts Edward had bestowed on me. They were wrapped in butcher paper and seemed innocent. They were obviously books of some sort. The special VIP entrance that Clarence had told me to come to, allowed me to successfully avoid the mob at the main door. I arrived at a checkpoint just inside the embassy side door. A young marine guard asked me what business I had with the embassy. I showed the marine my identification and told him I was here to see Clarence Clemshaw. He confirmed this by telephone and then helped me carry the two packages to the reception area just outside the executive offices of the embassy. I told the receptionist my name, and she said, "Come right in, Mr. Clemshaw is expecting you." Clarence welcomed me, put his finger to his lips in a shushing motion and in a low voice said "Follow me." The marine had already given him the two wrapped books.

Apparently the "safe" room was available and he wanted to save our conversation for a place in the embassy where we could have a secure meeting. We took with us the two packages Edward had given me. We walked down the hall and descended two floors in an elevator. We stepped out and headed down a long underground hallway. Near the end of the hall was a checkpoint manned by another marine.

Clarence gave me a temporary, embassy security clearance pass. I pinned the badge to my lapel. It stated in bold letters, "VIP visitor." Clarence had run down my CIC top-secret security clearance and updated it with an FBI background check, which allowed him to issue me a pass. The guard checked my badge and passed me through. Clarence punched in a code on the combination lock for the safe room door and it opened. He turned on the light and entered the room. I set down the two packages and we sat down and began to talk about the weeks events.

I told Clarence about my journey to Lanski. He was fascinated that I was able to find the place. He loved the stories of Peter making excellent vodka and Valdimer Zeiss buying some to take home. He said if he ever found the time he would visit Lanski and buy some vodka from Peter himself.

I told Clarence that when I was able to find the best way to deliver the Stocowski inheritance to the survivors, it would be in Polish funds. I wanted to send the money to him and have him give it to the heirs personally; I trusted him to witness their signatures. He said he would be glad to help out and told me about a company called, "The Peako Trading Company" with offices in New York.

This company had a deal with the Polish government that allowed them to exchange U.S. dollars at the black market rate, and send the U.S. dollars to the Polish government in exchange for Polish zlotys. They kept 10% as their fee, but money going legally into Poland in this fashion was a win-win deal for everybody. The Polish government participated in this program because before it was started, Polish heirs to foreign inheritance would leave Poland, legally or illegally, and get their inheritance outside of Poland. They wouldn't return for fear of reprisal. The new program with Peako had just started and was designed to keep heirs in Poland and give the Polish government much needed foreign currency.

I promised to look into the Peako Trading Company as soon as we were ready to disburse the estate. I told Clarence that I first had to convince the Washington Probate Court that the Stocowski heirs that I found were the lawful blood heirs of Stanislaw. After they had been approved by the court and an order of distribution was signed by the judge, I would start exploring ways to get the money to the Stocowskis.

I then showed Clarence the two packages that Edward had given me. We opened them and as I watched Clarence stare wide-eyed at the atlas, I realized I was very lucky to get it into the embassy without being noticed. He exclaimed, "Where did you get these? We knew they existed but none of us at the embassy has ever seen one."

He started to feverishly thumb through the atlas and then exclaimed again, "It's in English. Graham this may be the greatest intelligence coup of the year." He explained that the joint U.S.S.R. – Poland world atlas project was a top-secret project finished last year. It was rumored to have produced the most comprehensive mapping system of the world that had ever been produced. The smaller package contained an index to the atlas that was over a thousand pages with 300 to 500 place names on each page. They were all indexed to page numbers and grid lines. With ease you could look up a spot anywhere in the world, cross index it to the atlas and find it on the map by turning to the correct page and crossing the grid markers on the margin of the map. The most amazing part of the two books was that they both were in English.

Just to try it out, I looked up Lanski, which we were unable to locate from any source available to us in the United States. The index referred me to page 86, grid reference 11D. We turned to page 86, traced the grid to 11D, and there in tiny print was the village of Lanski. If I had had access to an atlas of this complexity, I could have done my heir search from Seattle.

Clarence acted like I had found the Hope Diamond. He told me, "We have a safe room with embassy officers working full time, trying to locate places behind the Iron Curtain. Now, in an unexpected stroke of luck, a lawyer from Seattle comes up with a possible solution to our research."

He said he would like to make copies of my atlas. After it had been copied, the atlas and index would be returned to me in Seattle in a diplomatic suitcase. He said I was probably watched when I came in, but he could re-wrap some innocent books about Poland in the paper that the atlas and index were wrapped in, and it would pass the scrutiny of anyone watching me leave the embassy.

With a little luck, the atlas might never be missed. He was so excited, he wanted me to share in the breakthrough the atlas represented for his staff. We took the atlas and the index and wrapped it again and left the safe room.

We went down one more floor and passed through another checkpoint guarded by a marine officer in dress blues. The Captain scanned our badges and let us pass. Clarence punched in the code on another steel door and we entered a much larger safe room that had maps on all the walls and several large tables near the center.

There were a dozen or more men and women hard at work pouring over tables with maps spread out on them. A lot of the maps were aerial photos with cellophane overlays. When Clarence walked in, one of the head supervisors came over and shook his hand. I was introduced to an intelligence officer by the name of Ike.

Clarence told Ike of the find and Ike said, "Let's try it out." He carried the atlas over to a table where three men were pouring over an aerial photograph of the area surrounding the outskirts of southern Moscow. Ike asked what had they been trying to locate, and one of the men said, "Lake Krotuva." The apparent group leader of the map search said, "We intercepted a Russian communication that a high level soviet meeting was going to take place at lake Krotuva in July, but we can't find the lake on any of the maps we use. We have been looking for it on our maps for two days and have just about given up. We have concentrated our search close to Moscow because most of the people that will attend the meeting are coming from Moscow." They had looked at every lake within 1,000 kilometers of Moscow on their aerial photographs and found nothing that matched. They were convinced that the name

"Lake Krotuva" was a code name for someplace else.

Ike opened the index and his finger scrolled right to the name Lake Krotuva. It was listed "Krotuva, L. (RFSSR) Page 20 - 13E." In a scramble the three men flipped the atlas open to page 20, crossed their fingers to grid 13-E, and there 550, kilometers southwest of Moscow was a tiny little lake. A magnifying glass showed the word, "Krotuva," to be embossed over the lake. The maps they had been looking at didn't even show a lake there. They grabbed their aerial surveillance photographs and with high-powered magnification were able to determine that the lake had been well camouflaged and could not be seen from the air. Without the atlas they never would have found it.

A shout went up at the find, and in an instant everyone in the room was arguing over who would get the atlas next. Ike said, "This is as good as any intelligence resource I have come across in Poland." I was warmly thanked for bringing the atlas to the embassy. Clarence promised to return it to me in Seattle within six weeks.

Before leaving the map room, Clarence pulled me aside and said, "I think you should leave Poland as soon as possible. If the map turns up missing and they arrest Edward, he might implicate you to make it easier on himself. Did you give Edward any U.S. cash?" I replied that I gave him $1000 in small bills as an advance on his inheritance. Clarence pointed out that this $1000 in U.S. currency was worth $2,000,000 zolty on the black market money exchange and it could trigger an accusation that I gave Edward a bribe for the atlas. It was obvious that I was flirting with an arrest for espionage.

The atlas was or should be classified as top secret by the Polish government. The U.S. Embassy at this point would never give up the atlas even if I was arrested and put in prison. I said to Clarence "Say no more, I'm out of here right now."

Clarence wrapped up some visa applications and some Polish travel books with the paper that the atlas and index were wrapped in. Clarence put in the exact volume of papers that the packages contained when I brought them into the embassy. He even made sure that the brown paper wrap was folded on the same crease lines. He sealed it with secure tape and called for an embassy car. In a matter of a few minutes I was driven back to the hotel by a young marine chauffer. I packed my bags for home and collected my passport from the front desk. It seemed like hours for them to locate my passport, but it probably took about 20 minutes. I paid my bill in cash as they refused to take my credit card. I think the desk clerk pocked my U.S. dollars and traded them for zolty. The two hastily wrapped parcels easily fit in my briefcase. I checked out and got a cab to the airport. I felt several times that I was being followed, but I never was able to spot anyone actually stalking me. I went straight to the LOT counter and was informed that the next flight, LOT 344, leaving Warsaw for the west, was departing in 45 minutes to Berlin. I gave the LOT ticket

agent my open ticket to Berlin that I bought in Copenhagen and he gave me a boarding pass and assigned me a
seat for Flight 344. I hoped I had time to clear immigration
and make it to the gate in time to board the short flight to
the West.

I would have to hurry through passport control. I
walked up to the bulletproof glass window of the passport
control booth and slid my passport through the small slit
in the glass. The guard inside scanned a list of names and
stopped when he saw my name. He went to a file drawer
and pulled out a manila letter-size file that had several
sheets in it. He opened it up and began reading.

A line was forming behind me and some of the travelers were getting impatient. The flight to Berlin was now
30 minutes away. The guard made a painstakingly slow
review of my file checking each and every line. With 15
minutes to flight time, passport control opened another
booth and the other travelers flocked to the new passport
control officer. With 5 minutes to flight time, the guard
asked to see my briefcase. He opened the booth's door and
I gave it to him. He was only interested in the two packages. With a sharp knife he slit the tape Clarence had sealed
them with and began to unwrap them. When he found the
visa applications and the travel books, he snickered and put
them back. He closed the briefcase and handed it back to
me as the door to the booth clicked shut. He was tapping
his finger on his desk and looking through my file, when I
politely reminded him that my plane was leaving immedi-

ately. He suddenly finished his review, stamped my passport and slid it back to me through the slit in the glass. He said to me in a grin that showed steel-capped teeth, "Attorney Taylor, it's a shame you fell asleep in the last act of Aida. It's the best part." With that, he laughed at me and I ran to the gate. I was the last one on the flight to Berlin.

I didn't stop shaking until we were in the air. The KGB knew where I was almost every minute of the time I was in Poland. Fortunately for me, they missed a lot of details. I bless my lucky stars that the atlas was one of the things they missed. Edward told me years later that when the atlas was printed, he made a few extra copies. He kept them in his personal safe at the university. He thought that someday they might be useful. He gave one to me in gratitude for my bringing Stanislaw's inheritance home to his family. The atlas was one of the most valuable things he possessed. Only five were officially made in the English language, I had the sixth.

All the way to Berlin I worried that the plane would turn around and I would be arrested. We landed less than an hour later, and in a few short steps, I was showing my American passport to several MP's at an airport security gate into the Western Zone of Germany. I didn't intend to stay in Berlin any longer than necessary – I was still behind the iron curtain. I went straight to the Lufthansa counter. Their next flight was to Stuttgart. I could not have cared less if it had been Madrid. Berlin was about a hundred miles inside the Iron Curtain and I wanted to get to the west and freedom immediately. I booked a seat and by 6:00 in the evening I was checking into the Holiday Inn in downtown Sindelfingen, a suburb of Stuttgart, West Germany.

The atlas did arrive at my office in Seattle, two months later, with a note of thanks signed by the U.S. Ambassador to Poland. I was glad to help. To this day I use the atlas when I want to locate anyplace in the world. It is, by far, the best atlas I have ever used, and it is still more accurate than anything available at bookstores.

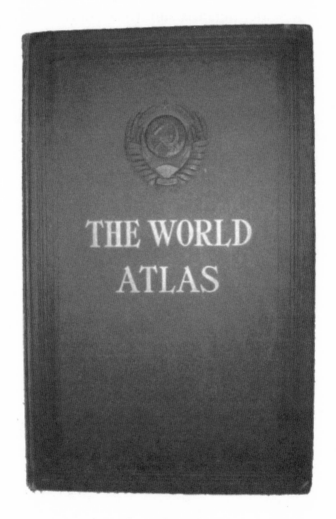

Edward's Atlas

CHAPTER THIRTY-FIVE

GRAHAM'S VACATION

The next morning I got up early and phoned my office. Everyone was excited at the news that the trip was successful. I informed my dad and secretary that since this was my first trip to Europe I was going to look around a little and come home next week.

Stuttgart is the home of Mercedes Benz. Its factory is located in a suburb of Stuttgart called "Sindelfingen." Sort of the Bel-Air of Stuttgart. A Mercedes Benz bus came right to the hotel and took me directly to the Mercedes Benz Tourist Center. They gave my tour group a nice lunch, free beer and a factory tour. All the promotional films, brochures and posters were silent about the role Mercedes Benz played in producing tanks, trucks and engines for the Nazi war machine. They showed us some movies that dated back to the turn of the century. My biggest surprise was that the factory workers had morning and afternoon beer breaks. However, I must admit I never saw a Mercedes Benz worker that looked even slightly drunk.

The Mercedes Benz Company had a European delivery plan for U.S. citizens. The cars were sold for about

10% less than the prices listed in the United States. I made plans to come back at the first opportunity to get a new Mercedes at the factory on their tourist delivery program and drive it around Europe.

After the factory tour I caught the Mercedes courtesy bus back to Stuttgart. On the way, I recalled that a Mr. Damiler from Stuttgart had sold Dr. Zeiss all of his exotic cars and I decided to find him. It wasn't hard, with a name like Damiler, it was like someone named Ford opening up a used car business in Detroit.

Harold Daimler sold the most exotic European cars in Germany. Ferraris and Maseratis were incredibly cheap in Germany in June of 1967. His highest priced Italian exotic was $4,500 for a 1964 Ferrari 275 GTS roadster. I bought the Ferrari roadster from him and a 1959 Mercedes Benz 300 SL roadster with 12,000 kilometers on it for $3,000. The Mercedes roadster was silver gray with red leather upholstery and just about the best looking car in the world. These two cars turned out to be the best investments I ever made. I sold the Ferrari before it even arrived in the U.S. for $10,000.

Several years later I sold the Mercedes for $45,000 and thought I had really hit the jackpot. I should never have sold either of the cars I bought from Harold. The 300 SL last sold for $250,000 in 1990 and the Ferrari brought $500,000 at a sale in Arizona in 1992.

All of the exotic cars of the 1950's and 1960's were scooped up by collectors in the early 1970's and brought to

America. Then the U.S. government passed smog control laws that banned all cars made after 1967 unless they were made as U.S. cars with factory catalyst converters and a mph speedometer. The arbitrage in exotic cars was brief and it was over before it started, but this fabulous trip to Poland put me in the middle of the best exotic car buyer's market in the history of the industry. It didn't hurt to have the dollar at an all time high in exchange for the German mark (four marks to the dollar).

I took possession of my 300 SL roadster and went on a brief trip to Rottenberg, a medieval town about 100 miles northeast of Stuttgart. The town is on the Tauber River and is nearly one thousand years old. I drove the 300 SL with the top down and enjoyed speeding through the winding roads between Stuttgart and Rottenberg. The yellow mustard fields and ancient farms along the way made the drive spectacular. I stayed in Rottenberg for two days. They were the most peaceful days I had spent in years.

When I returned to Stuttgart, I visited Harold Daimler and dropped off my 300 SL for him to ship to me in Seattle. He suggested that if I had the time, I should visit Milan. He had a friend there, Dino Mariano, that could get me a tour of the Ferrari and Maseratti factories. I thought that was a splendid idea and asked where the nearest airline ticket agency was. Harold took me to a close by Lufthansa office and I purchased a ticket to Milan. Harold noticed my plane didn't leave for 6 hours and he asked if I would like to tour the Porsche factory which was located just a few miles away. He said, "I went to high school with a nephew of Dr. Porsche and I can get you a VIP tour of the factory." I responded that I would love to go through the Porsche factory.

I was amazed at the difference between the Mercedes Benz factory and the Porsche factory. At the Porsche factory, the engines roamed around the ceiling on a chain and when they were ready to install one they stopped the chain and looked for the right engine. It could have been an engine made last week or last year. The bodies were all in disarray outside the assembly line. They were painted at night and whatever colors were painted were the ones that were assembled the following day. They did not seem to be building the cars in any set order. They seemed to be putting them together with whatever was available. The interiors were all tan or black and they matched up fine with just about any exterior color.

The Porsche factory was on a hillside near Harold's car company. We stood at the front door and looked across the Stuttgart valley. Harold's friend went to school with him at a school that they pointed out in the distance. As they were growing up they could see the factory growing and every day it served as a reminder that West Germany was rapidly recovering from the ravages of the war. I didn't realize it at the time, but both of these young German businessmen told me how terrified they were as children in 1943 when the American and British planes "fire bombed"

Stuttgart and burnt the city to the ground. They didn't believe for years that there was any chance of their city being rebuilt. Now they were in the middle of a tremendous growth cycle for Germany and they loved every minute of it. It seemed strange for three young men to be friends on the very ground that their fathers had fought over.

Dr. Porsche's nephew offered to sell me a car made for the U.S. market for 20% off of the U.S. delivered price. He said if I would put a deposit of $500 down I could pick any color I wanted and any special accessories that were available and he would make sure the car was acceptable for the new American "smog" standards that were going to be put into use the next year.

What a deal. I couldn't refuse the opportunity. I ordered a 1967 911 S Porsche two-door coupe with a sunroof. It cost $6,700 delivered in Seattle, shipping and duty included.

I got it with a leather interior and heated seats. These options were rare on U.S. delivered Porsches in 1967. The Seattle price of this car was $9,000, and there was a two-year waiting list to get it. I was also able to order a custom paint, "candy apple red," at no extra cost. When the car arrived, it was the most exotic car in town. Every time I parked it, I came back to find business cards on the windshield wipers with offers to buy it for a lot more than I paid for it. After the thrill of owning the flashiest Porsche in town wore off, I sold it for $9,000. The person I sold it to still has it, and drives it every day. He must have over 300,000 miles on it.

Even though the Porsche factory was very disorganized in comparison to the Mercedes Benz Factory, the new Porsche automobiles were extremely well put together. All of the cars coming off the assembly line were beautiful and well worth the price asked in 1967. Most of them are worth more today than their list price when they were first produced.

After the Porsche factory, Harold took me to the airport and stayed with me until my flight left for Milan. He promised to come to Seattle and visit, and he did about 18 months later. My flight to Milan took about 90 minutes and I headed for the Milan Hilton. After I checked in, I called Modena Motors and asked to speak to Dino Mariano.

A man answered the phone and we soon learned that he didn't speak English and I didn't speak Italian. After about five minutes of not being able to understand each other, he excused himself and the line sounded dead. I was about to hang up when suddenly a young female voice came on the line and in perfect English asked if she could help me. I explained that I was an American on vacation and that Harold Damiler from Stuttgart had recommended that I contact Mr. Marino about buying Italian sports cars to ship to the United States. She paused and began translating to someone nearby. She asked where I was staying and said that Mr. Marino would come by in a few minutes and pick me up.

I hurriedly showered and changed into casual clothes and within 20 minutes my phone rang with the message that someone was waiting for me in the lobby. I went down and was greeted by an elderly gentleman accompanied by a young, attractive woman. She greeted me and I recognized her voice–she was the woman that translated for us on the phone. She introduced herself as Maria Marino and explained that her father Dino could not understand English. He was born and raised in Florence, and when Italy was defeated by the allies, he withdrew into his old Italian culture and wanted nothing further to do with the outside world. In recent years, the family had made him realize that commerce with neighboring countries was good for the family, but he still refused to learn any English.

Maria was educated in Switzerland and spoke German and English, as well as her native Italian. She introduced me to her father and we shook hands but said nothing. Maria said she had handled all the business with Mr. Daimler and could do the same for me. We exited the hotel and headed for a large Maserati four-door sedan parked at the curb. We drove a few miles until we came to a warehouse near the railroad station. The driver got out and opened up the door of the warehouse and we drove in. It was dark inside but Dino got out and threw a large switch on the wall and suddenly the warehouse was as bright as day. I was shocked to see hundreds of Italian sports cars stacked on top of each other in shipping containers. There were

Ferraris, Maseratis, Bizzerinis, Lamborghinis and a whole bunch of cars I have never heard of. Many were pre-war but most of them were only a year or two old. I asked Maria where they had all come from and she shrugged her shoulders and said, "When sellers have to raise money in a hurry, Dino is the only one with cash. He always buys at his price and so he can sell them to people like you and Harold for a small mark up."

I walked around and saw several roadsters that I would have loved to own. I saw a particularly nice red 250 GTE Ferrari 2+2 coupe that was not even available in the United States. I asked Maria how much her father wanted for it.

She said, "Be patient. If you want to purchase any of Papa's cars, you have to do it the Italian way." Her father was walking up a staircase to an office in a sort of loft area and Maria beckoned for me to follow. When we entered, Dino went over to an old wooden closet. He opened up the doors to reveal a liquor cabinet stocked with several bottles of wine and liquor. He returned with three small glasses and a bottle of Amaretto. He poured a glass for me, Maria and himself. He then went over to a stereo set and turned on some music. We sat there in silence and I looked at Maria and I could see she wanted me to be patient. After about five minutes, she spoke and said, "Mr. Taylor, what do you think of my father's car collection?" She translated to her father what she had said and he smiled at me for the first time and nodded. I answered that it was the finest I had ever seen. She again translated and Dino stood up and shook my hand. Then she asked which one did I like the best. I started to say the red 250 GTE but she stopped me. I was supposed to talk in general terms about all the cars I liked and in a little while, make it known what I would pay for certain ones, and then Dino would decide what cars he would part with. We played this game for about an hour and finally I cut a deal to buy the red 250 GTE Ferrari. The deal had to be paid for in Italian lire and I really didn't know what I was paying for the car until I got to an American Express office. It ended up costing a little over $2,000. When I got the lire together, I paid for the car and took delivery of it. I had it licensed and registered in my name and I bought a 15-day insurance policy on it. They sold those at the American Express office in the late 1960s.

Maria got me letters of introduction to the Ferrari factory and to the Maserati factory, which were both in the town of Modena, on the outskirts of Milan. I drove my Ferrari to the factories and got a VIP tour of each. They were remarkably different. The Maserati factory was putting its emphasis on sedans and a luxury market while the Ferrari factory was obsessed with building racecars. They were a world apart from their German counterparts. After the tours, I drove my Ferrari to a shipper in Naples. They shipped it to Seattle, Washington by a freight forwarder that assured me with every nod of his head that he understood perfect English.

A month later I got a call from a customs broker in

Washington D.C. that they had received a Ferrari consigned to a man named Seattle Taylor, at Port Washington, USA. The shipment was sent to Washington D.C. as that was the closest match they could make with the consignee's address. If my phone number had not have been on the bill of lading, the car would still be at the dock in Washington D.C. I had the import agent put it on a truck and ship it the 3,500 miles to my home.

I caught a flight from Naples to London and after a few days sightseeing in London, I came home on a Polar flight direct to Seattle. By the time I arrived I was exhausted and deliriously happy with my success in Poland and my car purchases in Germany and Italy. My parents thought I was crazy as the new Porsche cost more than they had paid for their house.

CHAPTER THIRTY-SIX

MY REPORT TO THE COURT

After I got home, it took me a week to settle down and realize that my trip to Poland was over. No more vodka with every meal. No more looking over my shoulder to see if I was being followed. No more struggling with other languages. I was back to boring Seattle and I could not have been happier to be there. My secretary was reasonably glad to see me and she was happy that the trip was successful. Everyone was excited about the cars I had bought that were expected by mid-August. A neighbor, William Douglas, had to have the Ferrari and I sold the 275 GTS roadster to him for $10,000 cash. I made plans to go back to Stuttgart in September and buy more cars. I also ordered a new Mercedes Benz from our local dealer on the European delivery plan and made my reservations. I planned to visit Milan and the Mariano family again.

I had lunch with Keiko and we talked at great length about everything that happened in Poland. I left out the part about my meeting Ingried in Denmark while telling my story to Keiko. That was private and I didn't want to share that experience with anyone. Keiko was extremely happy that we found Stanislaw's sister. The niece and three nephews were an extra dividend. I asked her to add up all her time and expenses as I wanted to get her a fee for serving as personal representative of the estate. I told her what my fees were and she approved them. I prepared a report and petition to the court that set forth all my expenses, the partial distributions I gave the heirs, and our requested fees. I also outlined our plan to funnel four of the inheritances through the Peako Trading Company with final distribution through the U.S. Embassy in Warsaw. The payment to Edward Stocowski would be delayed and we would keep his inheritance in our office in a trust account until such time as he was able to come to Seattle and pick it up.

I asked the court to approve our plan and authorize the distributions requested. I sent the report in advance to the attorney for the State of Washington, Rick Ripinger and to my surprise he waived notice of the presentation of the Report and Order of Distribution and approved it for entry. The rest was easy. I scheduled a hearing for ten days later and when I put the order up to Dutch Williams for signature, he signed it and said he could hardly wait to hear about my travels. We did spend a couple of hours, at a Labor Day party at my parent's beach place, going over all the details of the trip. By that time I had the atlas back and everyone wanted to browse through it. They made me tell the stories told around the fire pit over and over again. Everyone wanted to meet Riada and find out what their future held for them. Everyone was anxious to know when I was going to meet the love of my life and have a beautiful blonde daughter, especially my mother.

*The one happiest to see me when I got home was Maggie,
my two-month-old puppy*

Coni, Graham, Cirstan And Maggie

CHAPTER THIRTY-SEVEN

THE PEAKO TRADING COMPANY

I wrote to the Peako Trading Company and they were very receptive to transferring the funds to Stanislaw's relatives. We sent the funds to them for the four heirs that wanted their money in Poland, and they converted the money into Peako Trading Company Certificates after deducting their fee. The certificates were then sent to Clarence Clemshaw at the U.S. Embassy in Warsaw and he transferred them to the heirs.

They all came to the embassy at once. For Jana and Merzec it was their first trip to Warsaw. Aneskia had been there before and so had Peter. Edward, true to his word, went down to Lanski a few weeks after I saw him in Warsaw and helped the four other heirs get to Warsaw. Once the heirs had the trading certificates issued by Peako, they were able to convert them into zloty at 2000 to one. The Polish government actually gave them the exchange. I always said that the exchange was the most unlikely trans-action I had ever seen with a government agency. My dad summed it up by saying, "They did it with mirrors, but everybody came out a winner so what's the difference."

Apparently the Polish government wouldn't be

caught dead trading zloty for dollars at anything other than the official exchange rate. They were happy to pay 2000 zloty for one Peako Trading Certificate even though it could be exchanged for only one dollar. The answer was simple; zloty were totally worthless in the western economy. I know because the few I brought back with me could not be exchanged at any price for western currency at a Seattle bank. Poland had to buy some western goods. If their zloty was totally worthless to western banks, getting U.S. dollars from people like the Stocowski heirs was one of the only ways the Polish government could get their hands on hard U.S. currency.

Understanding this phenomenon, and using the Peako Trading Company instead of a Polish government money exchange, made the heirs from Lanski over a hundred times wealthier than if they had used the official exchange rate. A Polish zloty would buy in consumer goods about what a dollar would buy. For example, a loaf of bread cost about 75 cents in America in 1967. You could buy a loaf of bread for 1 zloty in Poland in 1967. A house in the United States in 1967 at $50,000 would be matched in Poland by a home for about 65,000 Zloty.

Aneskia inherited 170 million zloty. Peter inherited 85 million zloty. Jana, Merzec and Riadia each received 56 million zloty. Edward preferred to keep his money in dollars in the United States. His $42,500 was in Seattle drawing interest in my trust account. Some may question whether he made the right move, but his freedom was more important than the extra money he could have received had he chosen to trade dollars for zloty with the Peako Trading Company.

Edward was the only heir that escaped from Poland. Without his inheritance from Stanislaw, he was doomed to a life of hard work in the research department of a run-down hospital in Warsaw.

1968 Mercedes-Benz 280SE
The car I ordered, the next year for European delivery.

Old Warsaw Were We Had Lunch

CHAPTER THIRTY-EIGHT

AFTER THE INHERITANCE

The Lanski heirs were rich beyond their wildest dreams. The exchange rate from the Peako Trading Company was a deal that was available only for a short period of time. When the Polish Government no longer needed U.S. dollars, the exchange rate reverted to the official rate. There was a narrow window of opportunity and the Stocowski heirs slipped through it. The money that Stanislaw saved brought his family into the 20th century. The following information about the Stocowski heirs was told to me by Edward when he came to Seattle to collect his inheritance. In many respects, I feel the money ruined the simple peasant life of the Lanski heirs. It made them yuppie Polish citizens who spent their money foolishly attempting to emulate a western lifestyle. Their zloty were at high buying power for basic items such as food, clothing, fuel and housing. When they tried to buy western consumer goods such as automobiles, TV sets, or refrigerators their zloty were just as worthless as their government's zloty.

At first, the urge to get beyond Lanski took hold of Peter, Jana and Merzec. Jana and her husband Ivan went to excessively drinking and eating and were close to becoming alcoholics. Their Catholic heritage saved them. With the guidance of a local priest, Jana and Ivan took the money they had left and went back to Lanski. As far as Edward knew, they are still there and work for Peter's vodka company.

Peter developed his vodka business and began a company that specialized in flavored vodkas. They are now sold all over Europe and even imported into the United States. The company purposefully stayed small and is doing very well. He is very successful and his inheritance became the stepping-stone for a thriving Lanski business. He and his wife Konara built a small commercial distillery in Lanski. They bought a generator for power and developed an industry that employed everyone in the village that wanted a job.

Merzec went to Krakow and bought a small business that manufactured wooden nesting dolls. He more or less traded his place in Lanski for one in Krakow with the main difference being that he had electric lights and running water. He raised a family and bought a small home that provided a permanent place for his family. His business has been successful and he and his family still live in Krakow.

Aneskia and Riadia stayed in Lanski for a while until Aneskia died in 1970. She died suddenly of a stroke and didn't suffer. Aneskia left all her inheritance to Riadia. Jana and Ivan had not yet returned to Lanski. With most of her adoptive family gone and with Peter and Konara wrapped up in their vodka business, Riadia felt out of place in Lanski. She went to Warsaw and converted her Zloty back to western currency in the black market. She took a huge loss. With just a few thousand dollars she slipped across the Polish border into West Germany and sought asylum. With all the punishment that Germany had put the gypsies through in the holocaust years, she was speedily given a German passport and West German citizenship.

The last Edward heard of her was that she had immigrated to England and rejoined a part of the Kalderash Gypsy Clan. Perhaps it was time for her to pass on the "gift" to one of her own people. She vanished in 1971 and has not been heard from since. She had such a good soul and kind, understanding personality that I am sure she is living a full and meaningful life.

Edward, true to his word, visited Toronto, Canada in the spring of 1974 for an Oncology International Seminar. He walked away from his group at the airport and came straight to Vancouver, Canada. He defected and sought asylum and citizenship from the Canadian Government. It was granted because of his professional skills. He was hired by the University of British Columbia Medical School, for a position in oncology research.

He came into my office unannounced, in September 1974 to collect all his money. Our bank is in the same building as our office. Edward was relieved to be able to go down a few floors to the bank and find all his money intact and waiting for him. It had grown to over $75,000. After he got his money, Edward took me to lunch true to the promise he made to me at our lunch in Warsaw. Over a bottle of good wine, he relaxed and told me about his escape from Poland.

CHAPTER THIRTY-NINE

EDWARD AND MONICA

We went to Rosellini's 410, a popular Seattle restaurant. With Edward sporting an ear-to-ear grin and a cashier's check for his inheritance we ordered a great lunch and a bottle of 1966 Lafite Rothchild. I protested that the wine was too expensive and Edward insisted that it was, "his turn," to treat me to a fine lunch and an elegant bottle of wine made in the year Stanislaw died.

He told me that he planned for years to escape from Poland, even before I came with Stanislaw's money. He desperately wanted to come to the west but he never had any money and lacked the courage to leave all his work behind. I asked him "What made you change your mind? Was it Stanislaw's money? To my surprise he said, "No. I did it for Monica." He told me that after I introduced him to Dr. Zeiss they became friends, and he used to visit him on weekends. He also became friends with Monica and took her out to dinner on more than one occasion. He even took her to the opera when Dr. Zeiss couldn't go. They became close friends. Monica, as a Swiss citizen, didn't get a chance to meet many men in her job. Dr. Zeiss forbade her from fraternizing with the hospital staff as he thought many of them were informants or worse, actual KGB agents. Edward was different, maybe because they had met through Dr. Zeiss' Seattle friends. In any event, their relationship had blossomed into a full romance by Christmas of 1971. They were not lovers yet but they were very fond of each other and constant companions.

Then fate stepped in and created a situation they couldn't ignore. Monica called Edward in the spring of 1972 and said in a trembling voice that she was in trouble and needed help and that he was the only person she could trust. They made plans to meet on a side street near the university where he was employed. When he first saw her, she was driving her 250 SL and looked terrified.

When he got to her car, she was shaking so much he realized that she shouldn't drive. He got in the driver's seat while she slid over and crouched down in the passenger seat. They drove to a secluded park and she told him what had happened. When she got to work that morning, she pulled the window drapes open and there was Dr. Zeiss, hanging with a rope around his neck. He was hanging in front of her window. He was immediately cut down by the hospital staff and pronounced dead from apparent suicide. Before they could cover him up, she saw several bullet holes in him, and knew that he had been murdered.

She knew so much of Dr. Zeiss' business, she was sure that she would be next. Without packing so much as a toothbrush she escaped in her 250 SL. She did stop to get a briefcase full of United States currency that Dr. Zeiss kept for emergencies, in Monica's locked file drawer. She opened the briefcase and Edward saw stacks of $100 bills. There was easily a quarter of a million dollars in the briefcase.

Apparently, Dr. Zeiss made a lot of money by exchanging western currency for zloty. When he left Poland for various medical meetings, he would take his prosthesis business with him. He could sell the artificial limbs he made in Poland for western currency and smuggle it back in his medical bags. Then he would exchange it at the black market rate of 2000 to 1 and sell the zloty to foreign doctors that came to Warsaw to visit and study his techniques.

Edward said that Dr. Zeiss was killed by the KGB for his flamboyant life style. Not only did he make a lot of money by selling medical supplies to the west, he waved his prosperity in the Polish government's face by buying expensive cars and racing them through the streets of Warsaw. Because of his popularity as a Polish hero, the KGB had to make it look like suicide or they would have had a revolution on their hands. No wonder Monica was terrified, she knew all about Dr. Ziess and where his money really came from.

Edward knew Monica had to escape immediately and he was the only one that could help her. He knew they had to be careful or they could both end up in prison. Edward called his office at Warsaw University and told them he would be gone for a few days to tend to a family emergency. He was able to slip away unnoticed as he had a lot of vacation time saved up and deserved a short work break.

Edward drove Monica to Lanski on back roads under cover of darkness and a violent storm. They stayed at Aneskia's empty house and hid from everyone. After a few days at Lanski, Edward and Monica committed themselves to each other and became lovers. He asked her to marry him and she accepted.

Because of Peter's successful vodka business, Lanski was not as remote as it used to be. Edward knew that he had to get Monica out of Poland soon, or they would be discovered. They knew they had enough money to escape to the West. Edward's life work was at risk. They agreed that they would wait for Edward to join Monica until the time was right.

Edward had just a few days before he had to return to work. They had been hiding Monica's car in one of Peter's warehouses. One night, they slipped out of Lanski and headed for the Chezechoslovakian border. Monica drove across the border without any more than a cursory document check. She left Edward just north of the border and he watched her as she drove her car through with her Swiss passport and Swiss license plates. She traveled through Chezechoslovakia by herself and when she arrived at the south border just north of Austria, she passed herself off as a Swiss tourist going home from vacation. She was waived through the Austrian border into freedom by the sleepy guards that were more interested in looking at her legs than her paper work.

Edward went back to his job in Warsaw by bus from southern Poland. When he got back, everyone in Warsaw was talking about the untimely death of Dr. Zeiss. Nobody mentioned Monica, and even though Edward had been seen publicly with her, nobody made any connection between him and Monica. Edward was told by the hospital staff that Dr. Zeiss committed suicide and was cremated immediately after he was found. This, in his mind, confirmed Dr. Zeiss's murder, as Edward pointed out Catholics don't get cremated. There was no suicide note and none of Dr. Zeiss's' family could be found. Edward distanced himself from Dr. Zeiss and his hospital because he was afraid that his relationship with Monica would be discovered.

At first, Monica was able to get messages to Edward by having friends that were coming to Warsaw hand deliver them. After a few months she started writing him under an assumed name. Edward was ecstatic to hear that Monica was safe and with her parents in Zurich. They kept their love alive by frequent correspondence and planned for the day when they would be together. Edward's boss knew he had a girlfriend in Switzerland, but didn't know who she was. He refused to allow Edward to travel to any of the Swiss oncology seminars.

The seminar in Toronto in 1973 seemed the perfect opportunity. Monica and Edward made their escape plans several months before the seminar. When the Toronto seminar was first put together, Edward was left off the group from Warsaw University that was selected to attend. He bribed his section head with $100 in United States currency that he had saved from the funds I had given him. $100 went a long way in 1973 Poland. He was suddenly included on the list of Polish doctors scheduled to attend the seminar. He kept his fingers crossed until he was actually in the plane and it took off.

He knew he had to escape as soon as he landed in Toronto. He had foolishly cleaned out his desk and taken every shred of research material. His bags contained hardly any clothing. They were full of paperwork that soon would be missed at the university. He was sure that by the time they got to the hotel he would be detained and recalled to Warsaw. He decided to make his break at the airport. Right after he cleared customs and collected his bags, Edward went to the men's room and waited until the rest of the passengers had cleared the area. He carefully emerged from the restroom and when he saw nobody watching, he made his escape. He took the first bus he saw outside the terminal. It was headed for Montreal.

Once there, he called Monica in Zurich and told her the good news. They made plans to meet in Vancouver. Using the money I had given him in Warsaw, he traveled as a tourist on a trans-Canada bus. Since he was already inside Canada, he was able to travel all the way to Vancouver with out going through any border check. Monica, as a Swiss citizen, had no problem getting into Canada and was even granted a permanent work visa. Edward applied for a visa exemption as a political refugee and with a short review and a one hour hearing, his request was granted. He applied for and received Canadian citizenship a short time later.

They have lived together ever since. They bought a house with the Zeiss money Monica was able to smuggle out of Poland. Edward and Monica were married in Vancouver on August 15, 1974. Now that they finally were free, they planed to raise a family and settle down in Canada for the rest of their lives.

At the time we met in 1974, they were both working for the University of British Columbia. Edward was working in oncology research and Monica was teaching in the language department. She taught students taking Chinese and Japanese language courses. She had mastered these languages in Switzerland while waiting for Edward.

Edward thanked me for helping him and the rest of his family and shook my hand and left my office. I tried to look them up in the early 1980s while on a trip to Vancouver but by then, they had left the university and moved back to Toronto.

My meeting with Edward in 1974 is the last contact I had with any of the heirs of Stanislaw Stocowski.

Monica's 250 SL

EPILOGUE

My experiences in Poland have been part of my daily thoughts for the last thirty-five years. The events in Lanski really happened and the prophesies that Riadia related all came true. I have always felt that there is a special "gift" that some people possess. The mental telepathy that is often experienced when close family members sense things are happening to other family members is a form of communication that exists in this world and beyond. Riadia developed this ability to communicate to a high level. I was lucky to have met her and experience her psychic powers.

I feel this story wouldn't be complete without telling you what happened to Ingried. She came to Seattle a few months after I came back from Poland. She took an educational leave of absence from SAS and entered the United States on a student visa. She enrolled at the University of Washington in Seattle and we became close personal friends. Our romance didn't last. We dated a few times but I was into the business world while she was enjoying university life. We decided soon after she arrived in Seattle, that our relationship was much better as friends than as lovers. She graduated from the university in 1973 with a degree in law and business. I helped her get a job as a paralegal. She worked for a large law firm that I recommended to her. We remained good friends and I saw her quite often. She never gave up her dream of becoming a California girl.

My best friend from high school, Hairstone Oliver (Harry) was living in California. Harry and I were inseparable pals from grade school until we graduated from high school. He joined the Army and I went on to college and eventually law school. We kept in touch and I used to marvel at his exploits. Harry had done just about everything a person could do after his graduation from high school. He was a Green Beret and helicopter pilot in the Korean war, a pilot for Flying Tiger Air Cargo in Formosa after the war, and even flew a P-51 fighter as a mercenary for a Latin American country during their revolution. He served as a war correspondent for a newspaper in the Viet Nam war and got a degree from UCLA in computer science after the Viet Nam war was over. He was currently a computer specialist working for one of the largest banks in America. I wrote several letters to Harry about my trip. He was fascinated with my stories about Ingried. Harry sent back a nice letter describing how much he enjoyed my correspondence and how he envied my meeting a nice person like Ingried. A few days after I got his letter, I had a lunch date with Ingried. I read it to her. She wanted to know everything that I could tell her about my wild friend Harry.

I described him as a very handsome sort of crazy

guy that would do just about anything on a moment's notice. I told her he was the friend that my parents didn't want me to play with as we were growing up. We never got in any real trouble but on several occasions, we came darn close. We always seemed to emerge unscathed from our escapades. He wasn't married and had no children. I told Ingried that he will always be one of my closest friends. I think both Ingried and Harry had a crush on each other even though they had never met and had only seen pictures of each other.

In the summer of 1974, Harry came up to Seattle for our twentieth high school reunion. He called from the airport and expected me to pick him up. It was just like him to suddenly show up and expect me to drop everything to accommodate his schedule. Fortunately, my afternoon calendar was free, as I had reserved it for a golf lesson. I cancelled the lesson and took the rest of the day off. Harry and I went out for a four-hour lunch. We had a great time catching up on everything each of us had done since we last saw each other. Besides the reunion, he was in town to take possession of a yacht that he was going to outfit, and sail around the world. He had taken a two-year leave of absence from his job and was planning stops at all the famous beaches around the world. He invited me to join him for any segment of the trip I could get away for.

He already knew all about my travels in Poland but wanted to be brought up to date on what had happened since my return. I explained about sending the Stocowski inheritance to Poland. I was about to tell him about how I was holding Edward's money for him when he stopped me and asked about Ingried. When I told him that Ingried was right here in Seattle and that we were not romantically involved, he was ecstatic. From that point on, all Harry wanted to talk about was Ingried. He soon asked for both her home phone number and address of where she worked. I excused myself from our table and called Ingried to make sure it was o.k. to give Harry her number. After she said she would like to meet Harry, I returned to our lunch table and gave him her phone number and her work address. I invited him to have dinner with me and he responded, "Only if Ingried is busy." He left our lunch meeting and headed straight for her office. I later learned that he walked in, went directly to her desk and invited her out to dinner. She accepted. At dinner he told her about his trip around the world on the 45-foot sailboat he had just bought and she confessed that her life long dream was to embark on a cruise like that. He brought her to the reunion and, when he left town on his new yacht a few days later, Ingried was with him.

Their travels took them down the west coast and into Mexico. I traveled to Acapulco and was best man at their wedding. They were head over heels in love and were already thinking about canceling the rest of the trip now that they had found each other. They made it as far as Miami before Ingried was pregnant. They decided to stay. They sold the boat. Harry was able to get a job with the same bank he worked for in San Francisco.

Ingried got her wish to live close to a beach but it was in Florida, not California. We still keep in touch and try to see each other as often as possible. Harry and Ingried came to Seattle and stayed for a week last summer. They have raised two beautiful children, a boy and a girl that are currently going to college on the east coast.

As to my own life, Riadia's prophesy proved correct. In 1975 I was skiing at a local ski resort with a friend of mine. While riding up the mountain on a chair lift, I thought I saw Ingried ski by. I remarked to my friend that I know a girl that looks just like the one that just skied by, and he said, "Would you like to meet Coni?" I quickly learned that he knew the skier and that she was a flight attendant for United Air lines. We skied down the mountain and met her and one of her girlfriends in the lift line.

She was Coni Scribner and was born and raised in Spokane, Washington. She was 26 and had never been married. We spent the rest of the morning skiing and enjoyed a nice lunch at the lodge. I was infatuated with Coni. We agreed to meet for dinner and from that moment on Coni and I became inseparable companions. We were married a year later.

Coni loves old cars. When I first met her she was driving a vintage 230 SL Mercedes roadster that looked just like Monica's. We became partners and started a classic car company which we own and enjoy to this day. She went with me on all my later car buying trips to Europe. My law practice prospered and we live very comfortably. We have enjoyed a wonderful marriage and were blessed with a beautiful daughter that we named Cirstan. Our daughter recently graduated from the University of Southern California in Los Angeles. She is planning to go into law and become a fourth generation lawyer. I hope that someday she will experience the kind of legal adventure that I had with Stanislaw Stocowski and his family.

GRAHAM FITCH

1957 Mercedes-Benz 300 SL two-seat roadster

1960 Ferrari 250 GTE 2 + 2

Two of the cars I bought on my trip

1969 Porsche 911S coupe

The Porsche I ordered when I visited the factory in Stuttgart.